## ABOUT THE COVER

The stunning cover symbolizes a modern goddess giving humans a vision of "global consciousness" needed to develop a mature world. The goddess is female to recognize that surviving today's massive threats requires the feminine qualities of wisdom, cooperation and love. She also represents the younger generation that must lead this transformation.

# BEYOND KNOWLEDGE

## HOW TECHNOLOGY IS DRIVING AN AGE OF CONSCIOUSNESS

**WILLIAM E. HALAL**

Published in 2021 by William E. Halal

Copyright ©2021 William E. Halal

Publisher: Foresight Books

ISBN: 978-1-7372950-1-3 (Paperback)

Cover design & interior crafted with love by the team at:
www.myebook.online

William E. Halal has asserted his rights to be identified as the author of this work in accordance with the Copyright, Designs and Pattern Act 1998

# DEDICATION

*To all the visionaries, prophets, do-gooders and malcontents who have tried to show us the prospect of a better world. Rejoice ! Your time has come.*

# ACKNOWLEDGEMENTS

I am grateful for the many colleagues and friends who read parts of the manuscript and offered their constructive thoughts. GWU Professor Pradeep Rau provided encouragement and detailed comments. Special thanks go to Hazel Henderson, Michael Lee and Amy Fletcher for having the confidence to write forewords; Michael also inspired me with his unflagging support throughout the book's development. Nina Amir helped with the book proposal, and Micha Rahder used her editorial skills to improve the manuscript. Don Fehr at Trident Media Literary Agency provided some tough love on strong proposals, which forged a better Introduction. Steve Piersanti, founder of Berrett-Koehler Publishers, gave me advice on the new realities of book publishing today. My previous publisher, Palgrave Macmillan, authorized adapting part of my previous book, *Technology's Promise*. My deepest thanks are reserved for Owen Davies, my long-time friend and associate, who provided his usual excellent advice when reviewing the manuscript. Lastly, I owe heaps of gratitude to Dave Henderson at *MYeBook* and my partner, Angus Hooke, for helping my publisher, **Foresight Books**, bring *Beyond Knowledge* to the public in fine shape.

# CONTENTS

FOREWORDS

# A Highly Original Exploration of the Next Stage in Human Evolution

## By Hazel Henderson

I enjoyed this book immensely. As a colleague of Professor Halal some years ago on a tech forecasting project within the World Future Society, I was happy to re-connect and write this Foreword.

*Beyond Knowledge* is a highly original exploration of the next stage of human evolution, as planet Earth is now teaching us directly. As I have also stressed, the planet is our programmed learning environment, mirroring back to humans the global problems we have caused due to our limited perception. This feedback from planet Earth is forcing us to mature, as Halal describes in such innovative and useful detail. We are looking at ourselves and learning to assess in new ways our limited cognition, our emotions, our continual conscious and sub-conscious processing of the realities of our condition. The growing calamities of floods, fires, superstorms, biodiversity losses, species extinctions and more frequently zoonotic viruses and the COVID-19 Pandemic are Nature's current lessons and feedbacks to assist our cognitive and spiritual development.

As Halal points out, if we cannot evolve to overcome our cognitive and emotional infancy and mature into full, wise adulthood, we will not survive. I agree and believe that many other species will take over the constantly evolving life processes of planet Earth. I was forced to confront the "Global MegaCrisis" that Halal and our mutual friend and colleague, futurist Michael Marien, have described so succinctly.

William Halal's deep dive into how humans have evolved over millennia and created our technological tools is enlightening and demonstrates high ethical principles for examining the ways we must change and mature into deeper consciousness. Halal shows how our new information tools are reflecting back our need to examine our own consciousness and how we must evolve beyond acquiring scientific knowledge toward also studying our belief systems, our religions and spiritual motivations.

This indeed, is the next page of the human agenda open before us. This task far outweighs the mad dash of trivial innovations geared to short-term profits so typical of Silicon Valley's adolescent culture. Halal instead offers his own innovative approach: seeing and assessing our technologies as our latest "tools of consciousness"! This goes far beyond the remit of such government research agencies as the US Office of Technology Assessment (OTA) which was shut down in 1996, slaying the messenger informing us of our planetary depredations. I served on OTA's Technology Assessment Advisory Council, and I am heartened that the 116th US Congress has an effort by over forty members to reinstate and fund OTA, and the Biden Administration seems equally committed.

Meanwhile, I have taken Halal's now tool to heart. This "tools of consciousness" approach has helped me see myself, my daily work and my virtual electronic presentations more clearly. I better understand my moods, attitudes, physical fitness and my preparations for my company's succession, as well as my coming experience of leaving this incarnation and going virtual.

In all the chapters of *Beyond Knowledge*, Halal uses this guiding spiritual consciousness framework to explore how we humans are progressing along the path to the kind of wisdom and maturity necessary to manage our further evolution in the Age of the Anthropocene.

Halal's chapters on "Uniting Science and Spirit," "A New Social Contract," " Democratic Enterprise," "Virtual Education," and "From Religion to Spirit" provide deeper grounding in our current situation. They are consistent with the 16 Principles of The Earth Charter, developed since its launch at the Earth Summit in 1992, and ratified by thousands of NGOs, academics, government officials, cities, investors and business leaders. I attended its launch in 2000 at the Peace Palace in The Hague and still remain an advocate of this universal declaration of human responsibilities to complement Eleanor Roosevelt's effort in the United Nations Declaration of Human Rights. No rights without responsibilities, as we are learning!

This book is a wise contribution to the great global debate on the Global MegaCrisis. It is also a feast and an enduring roadmap to guide the human family toward a sane, viable sustainable future. We are living through stressful times, yet stress is evolution's tool forcing species to adapt, and breakdowns drive breakthroughs!

**Hazel Henderson** is a global futurist and her eleven books and current research continue to map the worldwide transition from the fossil-fueled Industrial Era to the renewable circular economies emerging in a knowledge-rich, cleaner, greener and wiser future. Ethical Markets Media Certified B. Corporation, which Hazel founded in 2004 after 20 years advising the Calvert Group of socially-responsible mutual funds, continues the work of reforming markets and metrics to guide investors toward our long-term survival on planet Earth. In the 1960s, with the help of a volunteer ad agency and enlightened media executives, Hazel organized Citizens for Clean Air to inform New Yorkers of the polluted air they were breathing. They showed the late Robert F. Kennedy, then running for his Senate seat, all the sources of this pollution and why they were campaigning to correct the GDP to subtract, not add, these pollution costs. Kennedy's speech on the GDP problem at the University of Kansas became a rallying cry for reform of this obsolete indicator, still too often quoted as a measure of national "progress"! In 1975, Hazel joined Lester Brown on the founding board of the World Watch Institute, and again, she was forced to face up to this Global MegaCrisis at every board meeting, as the human effects on planetary ecosystems deteriorated. For more, see Hazel's recent presentation at the Family Office Forum in Singapore, March 5th. Hazel can be reached at hazel.henderson@ethicalmarkets.com

# The best handbook for understanding the future since Alvin Toffler's *Future Shock*

## By Michael Lee

At long last, a coherent visionary has appeared who can interpret the signs of the times and point to an alternative pathway to take humanity out of a dysfunctional global future. Professor William Halal's latest work on emerging techno-social trends gives us the big picture of what kind of world we now live in and how humanity can save itself from a blind descent into irreversible disorder.

As a futurist who believes that the science of cause-and-effect applies to social life just as surely as it does to the natural world, I've often despaired at the lack of true foresight being produced in the field of futures studies, in the social sciences and in social commentaries nowadays. In general, the study of the future hasn't matured beyond scenario planning and the "dark art" of conjecture to gain the status of a science. At a time of accelerating technological advancement, this vacuum of forethought only intensifies the prevailing mood of profound uncertainty and confusion. Bill Halal and his TechCast team are a notable exception, providing a collective model of foresight that is a world-leader in the field of future studies. TechCast's body of work, after decades of observing and interpreting major shifts in technology and thinking, has become an increasingly valuable resource for a true understanding of evolving society. They have reached a very high level of global insight about changes impacting on human behavior which may prove to be indispensable to our long-term survival.

This uplifting book is Bill's distillation of an unparalleled repository of collective wisdom. He decodes all the impacts of technology on social behavior on the global stage, for the benefit of laymen and experts alike. It's reassuring to look at the shocks and changes we are encountering as birth-pains of what he describes as a new Age of Consciousness, a transitional time in history. Drawing on results of TechCast work, based on insights from 150 experts across academia and industry, Bill weaves his story of how the globalized world has fallen into a MegaCrisis. How did we get into this trap? More importantly, how can we get out of it? *Beyond Knowledge: Technology is Driving an Age of Consciousness* contains many unexpected and provocative answers and food for thought for policymakers, CEOs, industry leaders, entrepreneurs, environmentalists, technologists, investors, academics and strategic thinkers. For example, the book outlines how we can transform government, business and other institutions to steer society towards solutions based on practicing and applying a higher form of consciousness.

The reader will find himself, or herself, trusting Bill's voice as he diagnoses the core problems facing the global world and then shows us the way to a more promising future in the Age of Consciousness. Naturally, a time of deep-seated transition, as the Age of Knowledge comes to an end, calls out for a wise guiding hand. I've no hesitation in saying I'll carry his new book into battle with me. I'm talking about the coming battle to get out of the mess we're all in, with its youth unemployment, its threat of further job losses to the forces of artificial intelligence, its obscene levels of social inequality, its scourge of violence and its planetary vulnerability to climate change.

Given these ingrained problems and the general scarcity of foresight mentioned earlier, I can say "Thank goodness" for Bill Halal, for TechCast and for this new book – the best handbook for understanding the future I've read since Toffler's *Future Shock*. *Beyond Knowledge* describes how the technology revolution could become a force for good by giving society higher-order capabilities and by forcing humans to become more aware, more creative, more spiritual and more holistic in their thinking. This would enable us to win back some competitive advantage over robots in what could be called the Intelligence Race.

As presciently argued in *Beyond Knowledge*, a change of behavior, thinking and direction, a deep shift in ethos, is required to steer our planet and global order to a safer, happier and more sustainable place. All other options seem sterile and bankrupt to me. For these reasons, it's an honor to commend this turbo-intelligent book to all those who wish to thrive in our complex, challenging world.

**Michael Lee** has been CEO of the ATM Industry Association (ATMIA), a global not-for-profit trade organization with over 11,000 members in about 70 countries, since 2004. As a qualified futurist, with a Master of Philosophy in Futures Studies (cum laude) from the Institute of Futures Research at the University of Stellenbosch's Graduate School of Business, he is the author of *Codebreaking our Future: Deciphering the Future's Hidden Order*. In 2018, the book, available on Amazon, was translated into Chinese by Beijing Fonghong Books Co., Ltd, the first stock company in China formed by the merger of a private publisher and a state-run publisher.

He was one of the few commentators to forecast victory for Donald Trump in the 2016 US presidential elections on the back of a wave of populism ("Preparing for a Pax Trumpicana". August 3, 2016. http://www.infideas.com/preparing-pax-trumpicana/)

Lee has teamed up with a neurosurgeon to co-author an upcoming sci-fi novel about head transplants and transformations of consciousness called *Chrysalis*.

For more, see Michael's www.positivedestiny.org

## *Beyond Knowledge* offers robust hope for a new technologically-enabled era of human consciousness.

### By Amy Fletcher

I am very pleased to have the opportunity to recommend Bill Halal's new book, *Beyond Knowledge*. I have known Bill since 2015, when I became involved with the work of TechCast Global, an innovative forecasting unit that focused on the economic and social implications of emerging technologies. Bill has drawn upon the scientific, entrepreneurial, political, and strategic insights gained over the course of his impressive career to produce a book that is forceful in its critique of the political and environmental crises we confront but which also lays out a pathway to a new era of human consciousness and freedom. This shift from old ways of thinking about society and democracy will not be easy, but it is absolutely necessary if we hope to build a global order that can wisely govern a mature planet.

Only twenty years ago, it was easy to believe that the liberal Washington consensus would spread around the world and that Silicon Valley would effortlessly enable peace and prosperity through technological innovation. Social media platforms promised to enhance democratic participation and connect each of us to the global community. Today, that optimistic moment seems fleeting and perhaps even irretrievably gone. In a powerful chapter on the crisis of democracy, Bill demonstrates how both the left and right have devolved into a vicious political polarization that reduces most of us to mere spectators and elections to reality TV. We now face rising authoritarianism, public lack of trust in democratic institutions and mass media, and dangerous radicalization across political parties and interests. In the midst of this geopolitical turmoil, exponential technological change continues to accelerate, adding another layer of instability and uncertainty. Bill confronts these systemic risks and pulls together multiple strands of political and technological change into a powerful portrait of a global crisis of faith.

Yet after this comprehensive diagnosis of the fragile state of the current world order, Bill argues forcefully that we can harness the power of emerging technologies to create a new Age of Consciousness appropriate to democracy in the twenty-first century. He demonstrates how the automation of labor and the emergence of a post-factual world have converged in a way that requires both a radical shift in how we think about the relationship between technology and democracy and a futures-oriented mindset that transcends the short-sightedness of electoral cycles and business models. The changes we need to make now are not incremental but revolutionary. As he argues, from an evolutionary perspective, "existential threats like climate change are not simply great problems – they represent a crisis of maturity for a global civilization that must be faced to create a sustainable planet."

While its critique of our historical moment is powerful, *Beyond Knowledge* also offers robust hope that we can navigate these challenges if we bring a spirit of collaboration and a futures-orientation to the job. Unlike many of the apocalyptic tomes currently in vogue, Bill's vision of a new global ethics brings power back to the people, reminding us that we do not have to be swept along passively as atomized individuals. Democracy may be under extraordinary stress, arguably not seen since at least the 1930s, but the same technologies that so often scare us can be harnessed, with a lot of effort, thought, patience and goodwill, to finding the future again.

I fully agree with Hazel Henderson that this book is a major contribution to the great global debate on the Global MegaCrisis. I look forward to using it in the classroom and to recommending it widely as essential to understanding the existential stakes of this moment in human evolution. While this is a difficult and painful cycle in democracy as we have traditionally understood it, hope for a better future prevails. Indeed, Bill puts it best when he says, "this may sound too good to be true, yet I think people 60 years old today will live to see the coming of a unified planet and the triumph of human spirit, once again. Then it's on to the Space Age."

**Amy Fletcher** (PhD) is a professional futurist and independent scholar. Prior to launching A Fletcher Strategies LLC, based in Knoxville, TN, she was an Associate Professor of Political Science and International Relations at the University of Canterbury in Christchurch, New Zealand. Born in Huntsville, Alabama, in the 1960s, because her father was then a young engineer working on the Apollo project, she has been interested in the societal implications of emerging technologies since the cradle. She completed her PhD at the University of Georgia in June 1997, and worked as a Legislative Assistant on Telecommunications and Technology issues for Representative Tillie Fowler (R–FL) in the United States Congress (1995/96). She is the Associate Editor of Politics and Life Sciences Journal (Cambridge University Press) and a Features Editor for Human Futures (World Futures Studies Federation). She is currently working on a book that analyses the cultural history and politics of cryonic suspension.

PREFACE

# Blessings of Maturity

*B*eyond Knowledge is my seventh book, and it culminates a long line of scholarship that started during my graduate days at UC Berkeley. I was drawn to Berkeley out of intrigue at the Free Speech Movement in the '60s. That period remains my most formative life experience. What caught my attention was that the world was changing with the onset of a "post-industrial revolution."[1] To my mind, this made perfect sense. The evolutionary concept implicit in this transition explained so much, and it offered the prospect of a hopeful future. Although I have taught in various fields during my years as a professor, my goal has always been to understand the transition to a high-tech world. Here's how I sum it up on my website:[2]

> "As an aerospace engineer on Apollo, an Air Force officer, a Silicon Valley manager, professor of technology & innovation, and president of TechCast, I have always been fascinated with the revolutionary power of technological change driving us into a high-tech global order. My work is devoted to helping all of us figure out where this profound transition is heading, what it all means, and how we can get there."

One of my first major studies led to the Life Cycle of Evolution[3] model described in this book's Introduction. I labored over the logarithmic graph for years, publishing three different versions, and I consider it a breakthrough in our understanding of evolutionary change.

Another source of insight was my first book, *The New Capitalism*[4] and other publications attempting to map out the contours of business and economics in an Information Age. Using trends supported by examples from the leading edge, this work identified the twin themes of democracy and enterprise running through the myriad innovations that have flourished over the years. These two principles continue to form the central pillars supporting much of my work.

*The New Capitalism* also helped shape the research method I have used during my academic career. Based on a "grounded theory" approach, I scan for items of

1   The book by Daniel Bell, *The Coming of Post-Industrial Society* (New York, Basic Books, 1973) was prescient in laying out the sweeping changes of the time.

2   www.BillHalal.com

3   Halal, "The Life Cycle of Evolution: A Meta-Technological Analysis of Civilization's Progress" (*Journal of Future Studies*, 2004) Vol. 9, No. 1

4   Halal, *The New Capitalism* (New York, Wiley, 1986)

significance, cluster them into trends, and use the content to guide the definitions of key concepts. Then I use the collective intelligence of experts to assess questions of interest and estimate the "best possible answers."

The greatest influence has been my work forecasting the Technology Revolution. During the '70s I could see the beginnings of an explosion of technological breakthroughs, so I started a course on Emerging Technologies. With the help of colleagues and graduate students, we proceeded to forecast the entire Technology Revolution. After our first publication of results,[5] we were flooded with a wave of requests.

Having published a score of academic articles that left little mark, this wave of interest caught my attention. This striking response affirmed something important was underway, and I kept improving this approach until TechCast soon became one of the best forecasting systems in the world. We received awards, a full page in the Washington Post, a citation by the US National Academies, speaking opportunities and consulting work.

Continuing this line of research made it clear that the tech revolution was simply the beginning of far more serious changes. Michael Marien and I used collective intelligence to map out what we called the Global MegaCrisis.[6] Results showed that the present global order is woefully unsustainable and requires massive change, although there is much doubt about the prospects.

Perhaps the capstone to this line of study was the simultaneous election of Trump, our forecast of artificial intelligence automating knowledge work, and the failure to address climate change.[7] All of this warned that we were entering uncharted territory, a post-factual world where values and beliefs superseded knowledge.

This realization also brought back memories of a colleague from many years ago who was painfully ahead of his time. Willis Harman foresaw today's historic changes in his seminal book, *Global Mind Change*.[8] I vividly recall telling Willis about my

---

5   Halal et al., "The George Washington University Forecast of Emerging Technology" (*Technological Forecasting & Social Change*, 1998)

6   William Halal and Michael Marien, "Global MegaCrisis" (*The Futurist*, May-Jun 2011)

7   Halal et al., "Forecasts of AI and Future Jobs in 2030: Muddling Through Likely with Two Alternative Scenarios" (*Journal of Futures Studies*, Dec 2016) 21(2): 83–96

8   Willis Harman, *Global Mind Change* (Indianapolis, Indiana, Knowledge Systems Inc, 1988)

concept of a democratic corporation and being stunned by his response that "this would mean nothing without a major shift in consciousness." It has taken me three decades to understand the wisdom of Harman's advice, and I am deeply grateful for his courage in showing the way.

The greatest source of inspiration comes from my own maturity as I am now in my eighth decade of a good life. One might think age is an impediment to creative work, but the opposite can be true. Only now have I appreciated the obstacles to change, the burden of perseverance, and the struggle for wisdom. This challenge of maturity forces us to find the truth that eludes youth.

It is precisely because I can appreciate the blessings of my own maturity that I can help us see the imminent maturity of our planet. Without this, the same insight that Harman tried to pass on decades ago, we will remain blind to this great story of our time. It is a blessed coincidence that my maturation is in sync with the planet, and I am gratified to tell the story.

We are all quite sure of our thinking because it is all we know. That is, until we experience an awaking of consciousness, like St. Paul's conversion on the road to Damascus. This sudden jolt of awareness, the awakening of higher consciousness, is the blessing that comes with maturity, and it is also the underlying thesis of this book. Prophets have tried to teach this inner wisdom throughout the ages, without much effect because it is the most difficult of life's many lessons.

In fact, that's what makes *Beyond Knowledge* a tough but crucial book. It requires a leap in faith to understand the world of consciousness now opening before us. I have done my best to make the argument and to mark the path ahead. Now, dear readers, the rest is up to you.

William E. Halal

Washington, DC

# CHAPTER ONE

# Introduction:
# The Noosphere Is Here

The great Jesuit anthropologist, Pierre Teilhard de Chardin, has long fascinated us with his vision that the world would evolve into a "noosphere,"[9] a great web of consciousness enveloping the Earth. It seemed a lovely but distant ideal, yet the Digital Revolution has now made that dream a reality. As this book will show, the noosphere is here today, and it promises to transform our lives, our work, social institutions, the global order, and our very minds and souls.

Not too long ago, we relied on telephones and newspapers to communicate. We now use two billion personal computers (PCs), 14 billion cell phones and laptops, and two billion TVs. The information flows through 30 million Internet servers, 3,500 space satellites and almost one million miles of undersea cables. This planetary layer of digital connections knits eight billion people into a living overlay of thought – the noosphere.

Although the world has an abundance of communication, it is not a very happy place. Just as the Gutenberg printing press unleashed a flood of information that led to wars and the Protestant Reformation, today's deluge of knowledge has brought a "post-factual" wave of nonsense, government gridlock, raging pandemics, the climate crisis and other global threats. We will see later that a "global consciousness" able to handle such threats is likely to emerge soon. But, in the meantime, the noosphere has highlighted the limits of knowledge.

## Beyond Knowledge

You would think we should have been enlightened by the past two decades of the Knowledge Age, so why do people seem badly misinformed, emotional and unreasonable? Despite the great evidence readily available, many do not believe in evolution, climate change, vaccination and other established science.

Even national policies are often based on emotions, as when the English left the EU and Americans elected President Trump. Political "rebellions" like this are common, of course, with their own logic and patriotic goals. But today, the technology can amplify disinformation. Trump, for instance, gained power using digital media to deny inconvenient facts as "fake news" and "conspiracy theories." An entire cottage industry has sprung up to warn of this "Assault on Intelligence," "The Death of Truth,"

---

9    Pierre Teilhard de Chardin, *The Phenomenon of Man* (New York: Harper, 1955)

"A World Without Facts" and "Truth Decay."[10]

It does not help that large parts of the public embrace this confusion. TV and the Internet have produced what has been called "the dumbest generation" with a disregard for general reading in favor of news sources echoing their beliefs.[11] Here are some choice bits of willful ignorance:

- The US ranks near the bottom of nations whose citizens believe in evolution, with less than 40 percent saying they accept the science.[12]
- Two-thirds cannot name the three branches of government.[13]
- As of early 2021, more than 70 percent of Republicans still believe the presidential election was stolen, after this was discredited by the courts and Republican officials themselves.

Extensive studies confirm that attitudes, beliefs and values are shaped by a variety of well-known biases, allegiance to political parties and other extraneous factors.[14] Even hard-nosed businesspeople admit that bias in decision making is a major problem.[15] Demagogues use self-serving fantasies to blind people to reality and mobilize them into violence.[16] It seems that objectivity is a thin veneer shielding base impulses as well as noble motives.

> Norman Lear, the famous American TV producer, said: "We just may be the most-informed, yet least self-aware people in history."[17]

This dilemma poses one of the great ironies of our time. The Digital Revolution has created a wealth of knowledge that is almost infinite. The smartphone alone has made the world's store of information available at the touch of a finger. There is no shortage of knowledge, but the power of facts is badly limited. Knowledge cannot tell us what is

10    Hayden, *The Assault on Intelligence* (New York: Penguin, 2018); Anne Applebaum, "A World Without Facts" (*Washington Post*, May 20, 2018); Jennifer Kavanagh and Michael Rich, *Truth Decay* (Santa Monica: The Rand Corporation, 2018)

11    Mark Bauerian, *The Dumbest Generation* (New York: Penguin, 2008)

12    Ker Than, "US Lags … Acceptance of Evolution" (*Live Science*, Aug 11, 2006)

13    Susan Jacoby, *The Age of American Unreason* (New York: Pantheon, 2008)

14    Elizabeth Kolbert, "Why Facts Don't Change Our Minds" (*The New Yorker*, Feb 27, 2017); Yuval Harari, "People Have Limited Knowledge. What's the Remedy? Nobody Knows" (*New York Times*, Apr 18, 2017)

15    Tobias Beer et al., "The Business Logic in Debiasing" (*McKinsey*, May 2017)

16    Harari, "Why Fiction Trumps Truth" (*The New York Times*, May 24, 2019)

17    "Norman Lear calls for leap of faith" (*The New Leaders*, May/June 1993)

worth doing, or what is right morally and what is wrong. Rational logic does not explain why people are altruistic or selfish, kind or cruel, enlightened or ignorant. Knowledge can never replace love, wisdom or a guiding vision.

This rule of unreason pervades life, and it is rampant in politics. The US government, for instance, has been locked in stalemate for decades, though Congress has more knowledge than it can handle. Emotional issues like abortion, gun control and immigration supported by strong majorities have been studied to death. Still, gridlock persists because of conflicting values, reluctance to compromise, and hunger for power − issues that lie **beyond knowledge.** Senator Ben Sasse worried, "We are living in an America of perpetual adolescence."[18]

This political stalemate is largely responsible for the poor US response to the coronavirus pandemic. China, Singapore, South Korea and other Asian nations weathered the storm reasonably well. But the US mismanaged it so badly that Americans fear structural weaknesses in government could inflict more damage from other crises. The pandemic brought these systemic flaws on vivid display for all to see. People are frightened and searching for solutions.

Many are ready to break from a past that no longer works. The World Economic Forum called for a "great reset" in all spheres of society. The result is a loss of faith in the reigning logic, or ideology, of money, power and self-interest. These values have their place, but they seem unable to address the crises of our time. Climate change is starting to bite, more pandemics are likely, inequality is growing, and there is a growing sense that the status quo is not sustainable. The conflict over these complex issues seems overwhelming because, once again, they are *beyond knowledge.* They hinge on stark differences in consciousness.

This existential threat has shattered confidence in what Francis Fukuyama proclaimed to be "The End of History" − the fall of communism and the triumph of capitalism and democracy.[19] A variety of voices suggest this crisis could trigger a "collapse of capitalism," roughly like the "collapse of communism" in the 1990s. It also stems from the same fatal flaw − an inability to adapt to a changing world.

---

18    Ben Sasse, *The Vanishing American Adult* (St. Martin's, 2017)

19    Ishaan Tharoor, "The Man Who Declared 'The End of History' Fears for Democracy's Future" (*Washington Post*, Feb 9, 2017)

Communism could not meet the complex demands of the Information Revolution, and now capitalism is failing to adapt to this confluence of global crises.

## Next Step in Social Evolution

What is going on here? Why is the US, the most prosperous and best-educated nation in the world, so inept? How can great knowledge produce such misguided behavior?

These problems can be best understood as the passing of the Knowledge Age and the opening of an unusual frontier – consciousness itself. Knowledge remains crucial, of course. But today's explosion of smartphones, social media and artificial intelligence (AI) has created a post-factual mess governed by raw emotions, distorted values and outmoded beliefs. An Age of Consciousness is starting now, though one may not like its current form. Whatever one thinks of former President Trump, almost all would concede that he is brilliant at creating an alternative reality. He is a master at shaping consciousness.

A "beyond knowledge test" helps clarify the critical role of consciousness. If some problem remains unresolved due to values, beliefs, personal agendas, self-interest or other *subjective* issues – climate, abortion, gun control, for example – then the solution lies *beyond knowledge*. This simple test highlights how the disorders that plague our time are not rational problems to solve by reason. They involve all the messy mental baggage of normal people, so they must be addressed by altering consciousness. **That is where the problems lie, and it is also where the solutions are to be found.**

This is a bold claim, but that is roughly how the shift to a world of knowledge looked when the Information Revolution began a few decades ago. Back when computers filled rooms, I recall telling people that we were entering a world of personal computers, and the typical response was, "Why would anyone want a personal computer?"

Yet in 2000, PCs were everywhere, books on knowledge became rife and the majority of jobs involved managing knowledge. I am equally confident that an Age of Consciousness is opening up today, and we simply do not yet understand this intriguing new frontier.

Beneath this tectonic shift in consciousness is the driving force of artificial intelligence, the most powerful agent of change today. Sundar Pichai, CEO of Google, said "AI is probably the most important thing humanity has ever worked on ... more profound than fire or electricity."[20] The advance of AI is automating knowledge work, threatening to eliminate roughly half of all jobs and posing one of the most perplexing questions of our time: *What lies beyond knowledge?* As Chapter three will explain, everything beyond knowledge is consciousness. This historic shift in social evolution is illustrated by the graph below.

I have struggled with this problem for years, and the result is Figure 1 showing what I call the "Life Cycle of Evolution (LCE)." Similar graphs have been sketched in general terms,[21] but this is the first to plot the long-term evolutionary trend using real scales and real data. The logarithmic time scale is needed to encompass the billions of years at the start of life, as well as just decades today. Without a log scale, the shape of the LCE would not be recognizable; the trendline would run flat and make a sharp 90 degree turn straight up.

Above the fray, there is a direction to this accelerating evolutionary process, and the logical next step is consciousness. Roughly four **million** years were needed to found Agrarian Civilizations. Nine **thousand** years to invent Industrial Society. One **hundred** years for the Post-Industrial Era. Five **decades** to a Knowledge Age. And the past 20 **years** to an Age of Consciousness.

Today, the world is poised at the cusp of transformation from a society based on knowledge to one guided by consciousness. This extraordinary acceleration through previous stages reveals how the planet suddenly came alive in a flash of awareness. The entire rise of civilization occurred in an extremely tiny fraction of one percent in the LCE. Historian Arnold Toynbee foresaw it as the "etherealization of life."[22] Teilhard de Chardin envisioned planetary consciousness to be the natural apex of evolution – the Omega Point.[23]

20    *World Economic Forum* (Jan 24, 2018)

21    For instance, the field of "big history" has studied similar time scales. See ibha.wildapricot.org (June 2, 2017)

22    Arnold J. Toynbee, *A Study of History* (Oxford Univ. Press, 1960)

23    Pierre Teilhard de Chardin, *The Phenomenon of Man* (New York: Harper Perennial 1976)

# The Life Cycle of Evolution

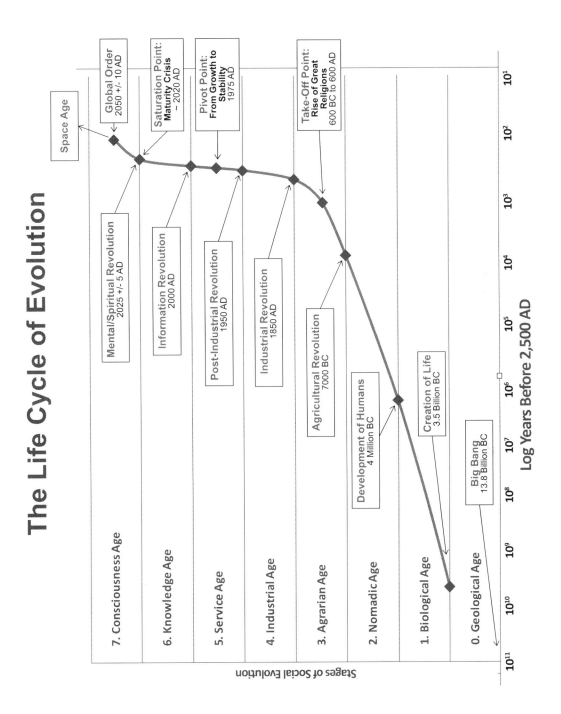

**Figure 1**

Consciousness has been around throughout history, of course, so what is really new? This transition can be understood through a similar evolutionary shift to the Knowledge Age. Information has also been used throughout civilization, of course. But the Knowledge Age began when digital technology matured about two decades ago into the most powerful force on Earth, occupying the bulk of the labor force, and our very minds.

In a similar way, shaping consciousness is now a powerful technology, although barely understood, and it is changing the world. Think of the explosion of opinion, disinformation and forbidden desires blasting out of loudspeakers like Facebook and Twitter. Anybody can use social media to shape public opinion, for better or worse. Politicians around the globe struggle to infiltrate the information systems of their adversaries, and they casually dismiss criticism as fake news. One analyst framed the problem this way: "In the past, wars were conducted with weapons. Now it's through social media."[24] The great challenge now is, how to shape a workable global consciousness out of this morass of differences to support almost eight billion people coexisting on this single planet?

This historic transition also poses enormous threats that seem almost impossible. Climate change and the entire constellation of end-of-the-world challenges comprise what I call the "Global MegaCrisis," or the "Crisis of Global Maturity." My studies conducted with a colleague, Michael Marien, find that roughly 70 percent of the public thinks the present world trajectory will lead to disaster. Ask anyone off the street and you will probably get the same answer. People have deep fears over today's failures in governance, and they attribute it to a lack of leadership, vision and cooperation.

> The late Stephen Hawking worried about "widening inequality, climate change, food, decimation of species, epidemic disease, acidification of the oceans. This is the most dangerous moment in the development of humanity, and our species must work together."[25]

---

24    "Quote of the Day" (*New York Times*, Sep 13, 2019)

25    Stephen Hawking, "This Is the Most Dangerous Time for Our Planet" (*The Guardian*, Dec 1, 2016)

The Technology Revolution will add even greater threats. The next chapter forecasts how advances across the technology spectrum are providing vast benefits, but also the enormous problems of "eating fruit from the biblical Tree of Knowledge." Smart cars, for example, will pass on the faults of smartphones. "A car is like a cell phone, and that makes it vulnerable to attack," said Jonathan Brossard, a security engineer. Many are horrified at the prospect of AI-controlled weapons turning on people. Now, ponder what could happen when billions of intelligent devices are wired into the Internet of Things?

The great S-curve formed by these eras is the universal symbol of the lifecycle. All living systems pass through this same process of birth (start of the S-curve), growth (upward phase), and maturity (leveling off) – a culture of bacteria, a growing child or the life of a planet. From this systems view, the Global MegaCrisis is an infinitely larger version of the same crisis of maturity that transforms teenagers into adults. Anyone who has raised children knows that teens may be fully grown physically and "know everything." But the typical teenager has not learned to control their impulses, struggles with inner doubts and can't cope with a confusing world.

That is roughly the state of our world today. Industrialized nations are fully developed, awash in information and with enough armaments to destroy us all. Yet they lack the wisdom to address climate change, regulate economies safely, curb terrorism and solve other nagging problems. As I will show in the next chapter, many people think we are heading toward a disaster of catastrophic proportions, and they have little faith in their leaders.

> Consciousness is not the same as "goodness," as is often thought by New Age enthusiasts. Like knowledge, consciousness encompasses all in its domain – including hate, conflict and delusion.

At some point, the stress becomes so severe that most teens eventually find the courage to grow up and become responsible adults. In a roughly similar way, the MegaCrisis is humanity's challenge to become a mature civilization. The world is being forced to grow up and to develop a sustainable global order – or perish. This passage to maturity is more than a historic challenge; it is also a historic opportunity.

Like adolescence, surmounting this painful process can lead to a better future. How could we let this singular moment pass?

## Triumph of Human Spirit

This evolutionary perspective helps us understand how a global consciousness is emerging today to resolve these threats and create a mature civilization. More than a theory, the chapters ahead will show how people are changing their lives, their work, social institutions and global mindset. I make a point of fleshing out these concepts with details, evidence, supporting examples and steps to consider. We will see how an Age of Consciousness is likely to develop into a tangible, productive and more meaningful way of life.

Consciousness is the inner terrain in which we live our lives, and it is changing rapidly to cope with the slightly crazed demands of high-tech life. People are embracing mindfulness, living with nature and using psychedelics to relieve stress, provide insight and improve health. I call these "technologies of consciousness" – methods that people use to guide their awareness, mood and understanding. The evidence shows that these techniques can instill the values of cooperation, understanding and compassion that are essential to a unified globe.

The main chapters outline how shifts in public consciousness are transforming the major organs of society – government, business, universities, religions and other institutions. In each case, I will show that a small *avant-garde* is quietly bringing a mature awareness to these varied facets of public life. Drawing on numerous examples, I show how business is turning democratic, government can be lean and responsive, education becoming student-centered, and religions moving from doctrine to a personal relationship with the spiritual world.

For instance, the Business Roundtable announcement that firms should serve all stakeholders is truly historic. *The New York Times* called it a "watershed moment ... that raises questions about the very nature of capitalism." Leading corporations like Johnson & Johnson, IKEA, Nucor Steel, Nortel, and Unilever collaborate with employees, customers, suppliers and governments to solve tough problems and create value for the company and stakeholders. Larry Fink, who runs the biggest investment firm in the world (Black Rock), directed the companies he owns to address social issues, even including climate costs in their operations.

These ideas may be reasonable, but many doubt such dramatic change is possible. In 2020, the "Black Lives Matter" movement began shifting attitudes around the world, illustrating that consciousness is changing even now. This push for racial justice is led by young people across the political and racial spectra, the cohort that favors global consciousness. It is reminiscent of the "Me Too" movement that ousted sexual predators, and the passing of gay marriage laws a few years ago. Big change arrives when the time has come.

The power of global consciousness provides the key to resolving the multiple crises of today. Each stage in social evolution has been propelled by revolutions – the Agrarian Revolution, the Industrial Revolution, Post-Industrial Revolution and, most recently, the Information Revolution. As my graph of the LCE lays out visually, we are now in the beginning throes of what I call a "Mental/Spiritual Revolution" to kick-start the Age of Consciousness. In short, it appears the world is heading toward some type of historic shift in consciousness, a collective epiphany, a new mindset, code of global ethics or a spiritual revolution.

> Civilization survived the fall of Rome, the Dark Ages, World Wars I and II, and a cold war bristling with nuclear weapons, and it seems likely to survive the Global MegaCrisis.

Such heroic change may appear daunting, especially at a time when hostilities seem endless and environmental disaster looms ahead. That is often the case before upheavals. Nobody thought the Soviet Union would collapse until it actually did. The evidence outlined throughout the book supports this evolutionary trend pretty well.

The reason this claim seems optimistic, perhaps even foolhardy, is that we have no experience in global consciousness. Huddled in our small section of the universe, humans have little conception of planetary evolution, much less the transition to a unified world. Our understanding is roughly similar to that of a naïve person who first witnesses the agony of a human birth or a teen struggling to adulthood. Without previous experience, these painful transitions would seem awful, too hard to bear. Yet they are entirely normal and usually successful.

So too could our passage to global maturity develop into a fairly normal transition in a few years. The LCE graph shows that a Mental/Spiritual Revolution is likely to arrive about 2025 or so. I am as confident in this forecast as I was that the Knowledge Age would arrive about 2000. This historic shift to an unknown era requires a new conceptual framework to map the terrain, a vision to provide inspiration and principles that work – the elements of this book.

A mature global order will still bear the normal human failings, but it will make our current strife look as primitive as the brutal reign of kings in the feudal ages. This may sound too good to be true, yet these trends suggest we will see the beginnings of a unified planet over the next decade or so, and the triumph of human spirit, once again.

## A Quick Guide to the Age of Consciousness

This book is not primarily about the workings of consciousness itself, nor is it mainly about technology, the future or other overdone topics. It is an exploration of this evolutionary shift to a new frontier of consciousness. This is a badly understood frontier, so I draw on the collective intelligence of academic studies, my state-of-the-art forecasting system and journalists writing in public media. Although my thesis applies to the world as a whole, I use examples from the context I know best – the US – although with abundant cases from around the globe. This is not speculative "blue-sky thinking," then, but solid analysis supported by substantial evidence.

This evolutionary perspective helps explain the big issues of our time. Today's age of unreason, global crises and the rise of consciousness can be understood as elements in a passage to global maturity. As we will see, this understanding resolves the ageless conflicts between science and spirit, business and society, conservatism and liberalism. It offers practical solutions to mass unemployment, climate change, government gridlock and other global threats. And, rather than some distant fantasy, it describes the changes happening now as individuals struggle to improve their lives. Once this unifying framework is grasped, the pieces fall into place and the idea becomes easy to embrace. We need a way to make sense of today's confusing world, and the emerging role of consciousness provides an intuitively reasonable framework.

Drawing on many years spent teaching complex subjects, I have done my best to present these ideas as in a series of informal talks, using quotes from prominent figures, including contrary opinion, and raising questions on behalf of the skeptical reader. The book is designed to tell a compelling story based on this shared understanding.

We now take a quick tour through the following chapters, telling the story of today's shift to an Age Consciousness.

## Chapter Two - Promises and Perils of the Technology Revolution: Eating Fruit from the Tree of Knowledge

Chapter Two draws on my work with TechCast, a state-of-the-art foresight system that uses collective intelligence to forecast the entire Technology Revolution. We can now envision renewable energy replacing oil, medical control over the genetic processes of life, self-driving "green" cars, computer power that is almost infinite, mobile communications at lightning speed, robots serving as helpers and much more to come.

The Technology Revolution offers unprecedented powers, yet it also promises unprecedented havoc. It would be nice to trust in what Richard Brautigan called "being watched over by machines of loving grace," but all technologies incur dangers. As we have seen, the smartphone is flooding the world with information overload, while social media is polarizing politics. Freedom House warned: "The future will be about controlling the masses through technology."

And a burst of industrialization is driving us toward a tipping point that could abruptly shift the climate. Extreme temperatures increase energy use for heating and cooling, creating a positive feedback loop. Perversely, this makes climate still worse, causing even more extreme temperatures. UN Secretary-General Antonio Guterres warned, "We are in deep trouble."[26]

26    Brady Dennis and Chris Mooney, "Global Carbon Reaches Record" (*Washington Post*, Dec 6, 2018)

In a symbolic sense, today's pursuit of knowledge invokes the biblical story in which Adam and Eve eat fruit of the Tree of Knowledge and are banished from paradise. The message is clear – knowledge exacts a heavy cost.

## Chapter Three - Uniting Science and Spirit: Technologies of Consciousness

Consciousness pervades life, yet we have only a vague inkling of what it really is. Here we reconcile the apparent conflict between the present scientific view limited to the physical brain versus "spiritual" behavior that is poorly understood. Leaving aside the possibility of supernatural powers, a pragmatic form of "human spirit" can be seen everywhere as a powerful facet of daily life; emotion, belief, ideology, vision and other mental states are very real and essential, much like physical phenomena.

The hard knowledge of science and the soft understanding of human spirit are not only compatible but complementary in crucial ways. Science shows that religious experience is caused by genetic features that have evolved in the brain. Other evidence demonstrates that spiritual practices improve health, performance and understanding. Neither alone can explain the complexity of life beyond knowledge. Accepting human spirit as a legitimate field of study would amount to a scientific revolution.

## Chapter Four - Democratic Enterprise: Collaboration Between Business and Society

This is a particularly important chapter because the idea of "democratizing" business is gaining traction as this book is being written. The profit-centered form of business has begun to appear outmoded in an age beyond knowledge. The focus on money that fueled the industrial past no longer seems to make sense when the most critical resources have shifted from factories and other forms of material capital to knowledge, innovation, human intelligence and creativity.

By recognizing the economic reality that all stakeholders are essential to success, corporations could become engines of both social progress as well as financial gain.[27]

---

27    See Amy Bernstein, "Shareholder Wealth vs. Stakeholder Health" (*Harvard Business Review*, April 24, 2017)

Moving from a profit-centric to a human-centric model of enterprise would be roughly comparable to the shift from an Earth-centric view of the solar system to understanding that planets revolve around the Sun.

## Chapter Five - A New Social Contract: Centrist Politics and Government Markets

This chapter argues that today's autocracies could be overcome by solving the problems that plague democracy. We will see that the bitter conflict between left and right could be turned into powerful centrist solutions. This seems a formidable challenge, but that is exactly what big shifts in consciousness are capable of. The Age of Consciousness is making this possible as the failure of both conservatives and liberals opens a new frontier for collaborative politicians.

We examine examples of creative policies that can fill the political vacuum between left and right. Green taxes returned to the public as carbon dividends could solve the environmental crisis while also promoting healthy economic growth. A well-managed market for medical insurance could provide a unique solution to health care. The same approach could also transform government bureaucracies into dynamic systems that better serve the public at less cost.

The problems of democracy and the threat of autocratic regimes may take years to resolve. But a new political consciousness of cooperation is needed to resolve the faults of our cumbersome democracies and unstable economies.

## Chapter Six - Virtual Education: The Uneasy Shift from Teaching to Learning

This chapter examines the shift in consciousness underway as virtual education (VE) enters widespread use. We will see how this transition drives the rise of student-centered teaching, new educational technologies, future career opportunities, games and visualization and changing university structures.

Schools are challenged to move beyond teaching and help students to become active learners themselves. The real work of education should embrace those complex skills that machines can't provide – understanding, creative problem-solving, leadership, and more. The head of MIT's online program called VE "the biggest change since the printing press."

# Chapter Seven - From Religion to Spirit: The Ultimate Technique of Consciousness

Although modern people today continue to believe in the supernatural, they are becoming "spiritual but not religious."[28] This chapter shows how a focus on human spirit is likely to transform religious institutions into a personal spirituality.

And since belief in higher powers, the soul, the purpose of life and other spiritual matters can so profoundly shape our views of life, spirituality could become the most powerful technology of consciousness, leading to a Mental/Spiritual Revolution. The rise of personal spirituality could even form the basis for a global ethics, or moral code, for a unified world.

# Chapter Eight - Managing Our Minds: Living and Working in Sprit

Here we see how technologies of consciousness (ToCs ) are being used to manage our very minds. As noted earlier, ToCs are methods used to guide awareness, mood, understanding and other facets of consciousness.

We focus on a few ToCs that relieve stress and provide insight: practicing meditation, living with nature and moderate use of psychotropic drugs. These tools for managing the mind can instill values of cooperation, gratitude and compassion that are needed for a unified world.

---

28   "Fewer Americans Affiliate with Organized Religions, Belief and Practice Unchanged: Key Findings from the 2014 General Social Survey" (NORC, March 2015)

# Chapter Nine - Toward a Global Consciousness: Start by Being Responsible

This chapter draws on a few outstanding principles of global consciousness to help guide the transition to a mature world. While people celebrate the freedoms of modern society, a world heading toward natural disasters requires individuals, organizations and nations to treat the planet as a sacred responsibility. We will also see the wisdom needed to govern the world as a unified whole, reform institutions, embrace diversity and celebrate community.

# Chapter Ten - Evolution's Climax: The Flowering of Human Spirit

I close by summing up how the profound shift in consciousness would lead to a flowering of human spirit. While the odds against this may seem overwhelming, it appears to be a natural climax in the flow of social evolution. A scenario provides a plausible vision of how the Age of Consciousness is likely to unfold. Other outcomes are possible, of course, but this is more likely based on the Life Cycle of Evolution. Life is moving in this direction and it is time to decide if we wish to be on the right side of history.

# Making the Transition: The Paths of Understanding and Personal Change

Readers may find some of these ideas are hard to accept. But the Global MegaCrisis is here now, and it requires a mature global order if we hope to survive. It's like seeing your child drive off with the family car for the first time. Or leave home for college. These are transitions fraught with danger. But they are also a necessary part of growing into adulthood.

We are going to need all the help we can get to meet this challenge. Absent some unexpected stroke of luck, the world is following a worn-out path that is no longer sustainable. Climate change is starting to flood coastal zones, scorch temperate lands, foster disease and famine, spawn more tornadoes and hurricanes, and provoke other extreme weather. With nations deeply in debt and trillions of dollars zipping around the globe at lightning speeds, it is only a matter of time until the next financial meltdown. The yawning gap between the wealthy and the middle class shows no signs of diminishing, and we may see more class conflict between rich and poor.

While these reactionary forces are pushing back, the world is also being pulled forward by the Technology Revolution, the rise of women to power and a new breed of young people who seem remarkably united across cultures. In the chapters ahead, we will see numerous examples forming the rough outlines of a global civilization. The alternative is too grim to bear.

What role do we, as individuals, play in this global transformation? There are two main paths for individuals making this arduous journey. You are taking the first path by reading this book and seeking to understand the task ahead. The second path is to use that knowledge to make your own transformation into a mature global citizen. This is all you can hope to control, really. But from there, almost anything is possible.

Now, let's start exploring the Age of Consciousness.

# CHAPTER TWO

# Promises and Perils of the Technology Revolution: Eating Fruit from the Tree of Knowledge

Technology revolutions have been occurring with regularity throughout history. The invention of fire, tools, farming, factories, printing, cars, electricity and hundreds of other breakthroughs started technological upheavals that were promising in their own right. Radio and TV alone held out the hope of widespread communication and learning, much like the Internet.

How does today's tech revolution differ from this historic succession of technological advances? Most importantly, some form of information technology (IT) has been used throughout civilization, so what is new really? Ancient stone hieroglyphs, papyrus scrolls, and the abacus were powerful ITs in their time. What exactly is different from these "old" technologies that makes today's Information Revolution special?

Where the Industrial Age mastered energy and matter (think nuclear energy and space flight), the Knowledge Age is mastering the third basic component of the universe – **information.** The Information Revolution is a pivotal shift in evolution that is empowering humans with unprecedented knowledge, intelligence and, hopefully, wisdom.

Knowledge is the very heart of scientific progress, and it is being harnessed systematically on a massive scale.[1] The decoding of the human genome, for instance, was only possible using supercomputers to manage the three billion bits of information in DNA. Information is the foundation of not only science but of *nature itself.* The discovery of CRISPR now provides a natural process for editing the DNA genetic code, with the potential to eliminate all 6,000 genetic diseases and create a cornucopia of life forms.[2] The ability to create any biological organism is at hand. That is the power of knowledge, almost akin to that of God.

> What is the difference between the Information Revolution, the Digital Revolution and the Technology Revolution? The Information and Digital Revolutions both mean the same revolutionary advance in information brought by digital computers. The Technology Revolution is the broader advance in all technical fields caused by this flood of information.

1    William E. Halal, *The Infinite Resource: Creating & Leading the Knowledge Enterprise* (San Francisco: Jossey-Bass, 1998)

2    Steve Conner, "First Human Embryos Edited in U.S." (*MIT Technology Review*, Jul 26, 2017)

Information is also unique as it can increase exponentially. Unlike the diminishing returns of the Industrial Age based on physical assets (For instance, factories), a knowledge economy draws on intangible knowledge assets that grow faster with each advance, creating increasing returns to scale. After Microsoft invests billions in developing new software, their marginal cost is about 50 cents to sell you a copy, spreading this technology around the globe. And whereas other tech revolutions were created by a small elite, the knowledge workers who generate and use information form the bulk of today's labor force.

The potential benefits of the information revolution are vast, but all technologies incur dangers. Technology is often misused, it produces unexpected problems, and it can be destructive, as nuclear weapons demonstrate. In a symbolic sense, today's pursuit of knowledge invokes the Biblical story in which Adam and Eve eat fruit of the Tree of Knowledge and are banished from paradise. The message is clear — knowledge exacts a heavy cost and demands responsibility.

Just so, we are now beginning to appreciate the dangers of the Information Revolution. As we will see, the smartphone alone has the world awash in information overload, and social media are polarizing politics into warring camps, allowing autocrats, and anybody really, to undermine democracies. As in any crisis, the world is poised between great opportunities and great threats, with the outcome hinging this time on how we handle conscious choices.

This chapter addresses these questions using a state-of-the-art forecasting system, the TechCast Project. TechCast's studies help us anticipate the vast changes ahead, and they also warn that this knowledge comes with difficult new responsibilities.

## Collective Intelligence Forecasting the Technology Revolution

The TechCast Project is an academic think tank that developed out of my coursework at George Washington University. It forecasts the Technology Revolution that is currently driving humanity beyond the Age of Knowledge and into the Age of Consciousness. The TechCast research method uses collective intelligence to pool the background information and the knowledge of roughly 150 high-tech CEOs, scientists and engineers, academics, consultants, futurists and other experts to forecast breakthroughs in all fields. Experts are selected based on their experience, educational degrees, publications and inventions. The experts are not all world-renowned, but they are all thought leaders representing the cutting edge of knowledge.

Unlike ordinary surveys,[3] TechCast's work is science-based. It draws on empirical adoption data, other forecasts, new research, leading-edge ventures and other relevant knowledge to guide expert judgments. To ensure that the analysis is balanced, we make a point of including opposing trends that hinder each development, such as political obstacles, high costs, or social resistance.

Experts look over this analysis, and they use their judgment to estimate when each technology is most likely to reach its next adoption level, the potential size of the economic market and their confidence in the forecast. The experts' estimates are aggregated automatically to update results in real time. More than snapshots, this is a continual tracking process that improves as comments and results help experts learn and as new data updates the analyses.

It is often thought that forecasting methods like this are subjective, whereas quantitative methods are precise. However, quantitative methods also involve uncertainty: They require underlying assumptions that often are doubtful, so results vary widely. In fact, we use quantitative forecasts in our background data, subsuming this information and allowing experts to resolve the uncertainty that remains.

There is no lack of strong and extreme opinion on technology breakthroughs, ranging from "That's already here" to "It'll never happen." This confusion is exactly what our research method of collective intelligence is designed to resolve. By integrating a variety of data sources and other forecasts, TechCast rises above the details to provide a broader analysis that is more authoritative than this collective background data. Experts may have bias, naturally, but these biases are usually distributed normally, canceling out in the aggregate results. In fact, collective human intelligence has the potential to surpass machine intelligence, giving us the edge in the coming conflict between AI and humanity.

---

3    H. Linstone and M. Turoff, *The Delphi Method* (London: Addison-Wesley, 1975)

This method of collective intelligence integrates all available knowledge and expert judgment to approach a scientific consensus that is remarkably prescient. If the present level of uncertainty about future technologies is defined as 100 percent, we have found that this process reduces uncertainty to about 20 to 30 percent. Validation studies comparing previous forecasts with actual arrival dates find that the average error of all forecasts is roughly +1/-3 years at ten-year future horizons. The -3 years error reflects the well-known tendency to be optimistic.

The results are compelling when considering the fact that the expert panel changed over this time, as did the prospects for various technologies. Prediction markets have demonstrated sound accuracy using a similar form of collective intelligence.[4] TechCast's forecasts also hold up well in our work for corporations and governments. On one consulting assignment, we conducted two parallel studies to forecast the maturing of energy technologies, one using a group of energy experts and the other using a group of general experts. The forecasts compared almost exactly, usually within one to two years.[5]

Figure 2 presents forecasts for 50 leading technologies organized into seven fields. Note that the percentages following each name (AI 30%) indicate the next adoption level to be forecast in the technology's life cycle. These results show that an avalanche of innovative change should sweep over society during the next 20 years.

## Macro Forecast of Most Likely Scenario 2030

Integrating these 50 forecasts to highlight dominant themes produces what I call a "macro forecast" – the strategic big picture. For convenience, I group the IT and E-commerce fields, and also the Transportation and Space fields, because they cover similar ground. For each of these five groupings, we explore the implications of these breakthroughs and their drawbacks. The result is an accurate but often worrisome assessment of the road ahead.

---

4   J. Wolfers and E. Zitezwitz, "Prediction Markets" (*Journal of Economic Perspectives,* 2004) 18 (2), 107-126

5   J. Laitner, *Energy Impact of Emerging Technologies* (Washington, DC: Environmental Protection Agency, 2004)

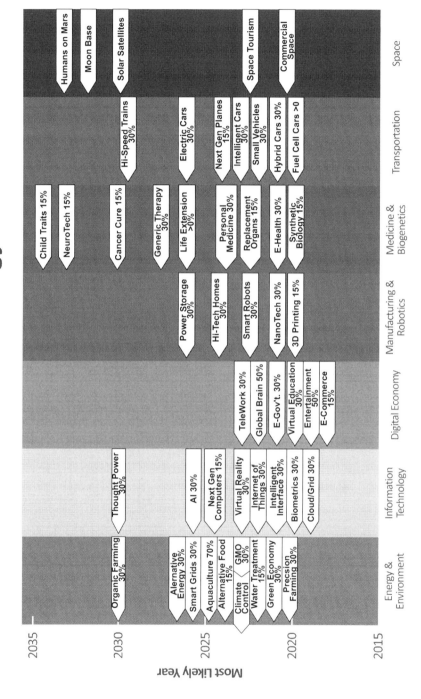

**Figure 2**

# The Environment is Both an Opportunity and a Threat

Changes in energy and the environment exemplify this chapter's theme on the Tree of Knowledge – many developments offer great opportunities but also great threats. Our forecasts show that green business is likely to take off around 2025 and governments should address global warming about that time. The global market for green technologies is expected to reach about $10 trillion – larger than automobiles, health care, or defense – creating millions of jobs.

Use of alternative energy sources – solar cells, wind turbines and biofuels – is growing 30 to 40 percent/year, as fast as Moore's Law forecasts the power of computers doubling every two years.

At the same time, globalization is expected to almost double the number of people living at industrialized levels, producing commensurate increases in energy demands, pollution levels, and global warming. The Earth experienced its 400th straight month of above average temperatures in 2020, and carbon emissions rose 3 percent, up from 1.6 percent in 2017. At this rate, global temperatures are likely to soar by 3 to 5 degrees C by 2100. The lower US, Central America, the Middle East, India, and China seem doomed to drought, extreme weather and rampant disease that would make them uninhabitable to humans.[6]

The IPSOS *Global Trends Report* surveys 22,000 people across 33 countries, finding that 80 percent think "we are heading for environmental disaster unless we change our habits."[7]

The problem has forced scientists to propose geoengineering the planet, using techniques such as spraying chemicals into the atmosphere to reduce temperatures, with their own unknown risks. Technologies to capture carbon and convert it into useful products are being developed, shifting efforts toward carbon *reduction*.[8] But

---

6   Damian Carrington, "Unsurvivable Heatwaves Could Strike Heart of China by End of Century" (*Guardian*, Aug 5, 2018)

7   Ipsos.com (Dec 1, 2020)

8   The push to reduce carbon is highlighted by the XPrize to be awarded for demonstrating the most effective means for turning carbon into useful products.

the task is enormous. It is thought that 9 million carbon-capturing plants costing $5 trillion/year would be needed to resolve the climate threat.[9]

It may require decades to turn global temperatures around, so, the big questions remaining are "How bad will it get?" and "What can be done now to avoid the threat?" Fortunately, people around the world are rising to this challenge. McKinsey, the leading consulting firm, finds that more than 90 percent of corporate executives agree that major changes are needed.[10] An executive at BP, one of the major oil companies, said: "The world demands more affordable clean energy… That's a major shift in our strategy."[11]

## Information Technology (IT) and E-Commerce Open a Pandora's Box

The revolutions in IT and e-commerce are no less extraordinary. Moore's Law may reach its limits, but a new generation of optical, biological, and quantum computers is poised to take over from current electronic models. These breakthroughs are bringing infinite (literally) knowledge and intelligence into widespread use during the next few decades. Artificial intelligence should automate 30 percent of routine tasks by about 2025 (+/- 3 years). Smart robots have pervaded factories and are now creeping into homes, offices and the battlefield.[12] The US military expects to have more combat robots than human soldiers by 2025.[13]

> Google's introduction of their advanced AI virtual assistant, Duplex, in 2018 was a stunning breakthrough, so humanlike it could pass the famed Turing test, carrying on a conversation without being recognized as a computer program.[14]

Collectively, there are now about 11 billion PCs, smartphones and other internet-connected devices making up the Internet of Things (IoT), which is expected to

---

9    Steven Mufson, "A Climate Solution Slowly Gains Ground" (*Washington Post*, Apr 21, 2019)

10   "Dynamism and Its Discontents" (*The Shortlist*, Jul 19, 2019); Adam Morton, "World's Biggest Carbon Emitters Told to Reach Net Zero" (*Bulletin of the Atomic Scientists*, Sep 18, 2019); Paul Hawken. *Drawdown: The Most Comprehensive Plan to Reverse Global Warming* (New York: Penguin Books, 2017) Also see Michael Marien et al., *Greening Capitalism* (Feb 2017)

11   Steven Mufson, "Big Oil Attempts Green Makeover" (*Washington Post*, Sep 21, 2020)

12   "Future of Employment; Will Robots Take My Job?" (*Oxford University*, Feb 15, 2018)

13   *New York Post* (Jun 15, 2017)

14   Drew Harwell, "A Google Program Can Pass as a Human on the Phone" (*Washington Post*, May 8, 2018)

control our homes, cars, offices, factories and any other gadget. But the IoT heightens the threat of a cybersecurity disaster.[15] James Clapper, US Director of National Intelligence, thinks "Intelligence services might use the IoT for identification, surveillance and monitoring."[16]

The disruption caused by smartphones alone should be fair warning about the greater dangers ahead. Mobile devices have created an online culture that increases stress and harms health. The World Health Organization warned that Internet addiction is now considered a mental disorder resulting in chronic sleep deprivation, less time in relaxation, less contact with friends and family, and serious increases in depression and suicide.[17] The smartphone has replaced typewriters, encyclopedias, fax machines, cameras, landline phones, yellow pages, newspapers, maps, books, disrupted the taxi and hotel industries, and more havoc is to come.

> Today's electronic machines guiding endless streams of electrons may soon yield to quantum computers using individual particles to control information at the atomic level, as nature does with awesome intelligence.

Control is tempting, which is why authoritarian regimes use the Internet to influence their citizens. China is using a system of "social credits" designed to reward good behavior and punish bad behavior. Author Kevin Kelly thinks this interconnected world will "give rise to a technological version of socialism," and another author, Yuval Noah Harari, has captured the hearts of CEOs preaching his gospel of "dataism" that will replace liberalism: "Infotech and biotech will create unprecedented upheavals and eroding human agency. Democracy and free markets might become obsolete."[18]

I hope the point is clear. The Information Revolution offers unprecedented benefits, but it also opens Pandora's box of security threats and challenges that require new levels of responsibility.

---

15    Bruce Schneier, *Click Here to Kill Everybody* (Norton, 2018)

16    "US Intelligence Chief: We Might Use the Internet of Things to Spy on You" (*Guardian*, Feb 9, 2016)

17    Jean M. Twenge, "Have Smart Phones Destroyed a Generation?" (*Atlantic*, Sept 2017)

18    Harari, "Why Technology Favors Tyranny" (*Atlantic*, October 2018)

## High-Tech Manufacturing Bestows Abundance and Pitfalls

The factories of the Industrial Age are yielding to intelligent manufacturing systems that churn out customized goods cheaply and quickly, boasting economic growth globally. The products increasingly include growing streams of intelligent robotic devices finding their way in nooks and crannies of life – the GPS navigation robot in your car, the robotic floor sweepers prowling around our floors, the military robots taking over the battlefield, a "virtual assistant" on your smartphone managing a busy day, the robotic surgeon who performs your appendectomy, and on and on. 3D printing is producing an endless variety of products, with almost any type of material, including bodily tissues with living cells. One report claimed, "Within a generation, you will have a hard time explaining to your children how you lived without a 3D printer."[19]

GE used 3D printing to build an advanced jet engine that reduces the number of parts from 855 to a dozen, sheds weight, runs on 20 percent less fuel, and delivers 10 percent more power. GE's engineering chief said, "Oh my God, this is fantastic."[20]

It should not surprise to caution that the abundance promised by these new manufacturing technologies comes with pitfalls. All this industrialized economic growth in developing regions, and even developed nations, will continue to raise living standards dramatically around the world. Although this global prosperity should be a great accomplishment, it is also the cause of the environmental crises noted a few pages back: mounting demands for energy, increased ecological damage, and clashes between diverse cultures. In short, we are likely to enjoy generous material wealth, but at the cost of difficult new challenges.

## Medical Advances Confer Mastery Over Life – and Big Risks

Breakthroughs in medicine are so vast they promise to give humans almost complete control over biological life. Just as the Industrial Age mastered the physical world, these advances are now making it possible to master the biological world.

---

19  Mihai Andrei, "3D Printing Could Revolutionize How We Eat" (*ZMEscience,* Apr 4, 2018)

20  Thomas Kellner, "Chief Explains How 3D Printing Will Upend Manufacturing" (*GE.com,* Nov 13, 2017)

The latest breakthrough is the new class of messenger RNA vaccines designed to protect against the coronavirus. Instead of using a weakened or inactivated version of the virus, the RNA is edited genetically to make a protein that triggers an immune response. This more powerful technology was able to develop vaccines around the world in a few months, instead of the normal several years.[21] It also opens up the realistic prospect of applying this same approach to redesign the genetic code that controls the behavior of all life forms.

A respected medical journal, *The Lancet,* projected that most babies born since 2000 in industrialized nations will live to celebrate their 100th birthday.

Electronic medical records, online doctor's visits, computerized diagnostics and other forms of telemedicine should curtail costs and improve health care. Anti-aging drugs, genetic treatments and other innovations are entering the market, and many now are confident that human life can be extended well beyond 100 years.

Synthetic biology is developing new microorganisms to manufacture drugs and repair spinal cord damage. Stem-cell technologies will soon be able to replace almost the entire human body with artificially grown organs, including parts of the brain. Biologist J. Craig Venter stated, "For the first time we are close to creating artificial life from scratch." Another prominent researcher said, "The future of medicine is not about blood and guts; it is about bits and bytes."[22]

Such power invariably incurs dangers.[23] Man-made viruses could wipe out millions of people in unintended plagues – or deliberate attacks. Designer DNA and synthetic biology could cause unintended ecological damage and produce dangerous lifeforms.

## Transportation Is Moving Faster and Farther

With ever more powerful IT systems making vivid long-distance communications common, one would think there might be less need to travel. But IT only forms a

21   "Understanding mRNA COVID-19 Vaccines" (US Centers for Disease Control, Mar 4, 2021)

22   J. Craig Venter Institute (May 25, 2016)

23   "Nearly Half of Surveyed Patients Worried Over Health Care Security" (*Health IT Security,* Feb 10, 2017)

virtual world that parallels the physical world, and people will always want to visit each other, handle the merchandise and hammer out tough decisions in person.

Our forecasts show that a new wave of self-driving green electric autos should become mainstream in the late 2020s.[24] Electric vehicles (EVs) constitute a true breakthrough. They are vastly simpler and easier to maintain, lighter and more efficient than conventional cars. An internal combustion engine has about 2000 moving parts, while EV engines only have about 20 parts. EVs are also expected to last 600,000 miles, and the cost is likely to fall to one-third of an ordinary car, with half the operating costs.[25] But the convenience of automated cars may actually cause *more travel*. Elon Musk, a leading developer of automated cars, thinks "…traffic will get worse."[26]

Developments in unmanned aircraft and electrically powered flight are now providing big improvements in air travel. High-speed trains and maglev trains are likely to handle 30 percent of fast traffic between major cities in much of the world by 2030 +/- 5 years.[27] Hypersonic planes using scramjet engines could travel anywhere on Earth in about two hours. International travel has been exploding in a global economy, but it is a curse in many ways. The flood of people crossing borders is the primary cause of global pandemics, terrorist attacks and clashing cultures.

> Airbus was awarded a patent for an aircraft to succeed the Concorde that will be capable of vertical takeoff and speeds of Mach 4.5 – over 3,450 mph.

Travel is also moving into space as control shifts from government to corporations. Virgin Galactic intends to launch tourists on suborbital flights, commercial spacecraft are servicing the International Space Station, and competitors are planning to visit the Moon. Peter Diamandis, who founded the X Prize to advance new technologies, thinks, "We're on the verge of the golden age [where] the public can tour space on a routine basis."[28]

The founding of a Moon colony is likely about 2030 and a Mars landing due about 2035. Some pioneers are intent on colonizing Mars, with no lack of volunteers, even though there may be no return to Earth. Solar satellites offer seven times more

---

24    "The Automotive Revolution Is Speeding Up" (*McKinsey,* Sep 2017)

25    "Electric Vehicles Cost Less Than Half as Much to Drive" (*Forbes,* Jan 14, 2018)

26    Fred Lambert, "Elon Musk on Autonomous Ride-Sharing" (*electrek,* May 1, 2018)

27    Matt McFarland, "Hyperloop: Transportation Nirvana, or a Pipedream?" (*CNN,* April 6, 2017)

28    *Office of Space Commercialization* (June 18, 2012)

energy than the Sun on Earth because in space there is no nighttime, no atmosphere, and no weather. These advances should lead to a full-blown Space Age by about 2050.

> Ralph Nansen of Solar High Company thinks, "Solar satellites are the ultimate energy source. I don't think there's any doubt that we will be getting the majority of our power from space."

Space may be an exciting new frontier, but only if we first resolve the Global MegaCrisis now blocking the path to this future. Otherwise, we may never reach the Space Age.

## The Crisis of Maturity Meets Global Consciousness

What are we to make of the conflicting promises and perils facing the journey of what Buckminster Fuller called Spaceship Earth? The Technology Revolution offers unprecedented powers at the very time dire warnings are being issued from all quarters. The Club of Rome updated its famous study, *Limits to Growth,* and the World Economic Forum published a summary of *Global Risks* that are strikingly similar in warning of vast threats.[29]

Professor Steven Pinker has pointed out the good news that wars of aggression, colonialism, deaths from combat and terrorism, homicides and poverty have been declining for decades, while life expectancy and civil rights have been rising steadily.[30] But these are gains over the ills of the past, and they ignore the far more complex threats of the Global MegaCrisis – climate change, chronic pandemics, financial collapse, terrorism, cyberwar and the list goes on. Additionally, TechCast's studies warn of wild-card threats across the spectrum – global depression, cyber-war, bio-war, and too many others.

Less attention is devoted to trends resolving the problems – the rise of alternative energy, the spreading of knowledge, women gaining power and young people becoming the first "global citizens." TechCast's studies reveal a surprising but intuitive

---

29    Ernst Ulrich von Weizsacker, and Anders Wujkman, *Second Report to the Club of Rome* (New York: Springer Science (Jan 2018); *The Global Risks* (Switzerland: World Economic Forum, 2018.

30    Steven Pinker, *Enlightenment Now* (Viking, 2018)

trend of movement toward social responsibility, transparency, environmental concern, diversity, global ethics and the like.[31]

We have studied this issue extensively and offer the survey results in Table 1, showing opinion across a pessimistic to optimistic set of four scenarios.[32] The first two pessimistic scenarios show a 60-percent probability that major parts of the globe will suffer the loss of civilization or enter a high-tech dark age. People are feeling deep anxiety over looming crises and entrenched failures in governance. They attribute these failures to a lack of leadership, political will, vision, and cooperation, offering little hope in finding a way through this impasse. There is a pervasive fear that we can't get our act together and that events could spin out of control.

Crisis serves to drive change, and the Global MegaCrisis is now causing a wrenching upheaval. Even now, climate change is beginning to force political action. Automation could soon eliminate as many as half of today's jobs, leaving governments struggling to find new forms of work for their citizens. Levels of national debt in major nations are precariously high and could easily precipitate another crisis like the 2008 financial meltdown, while conflict and war could escalate over limited resources. These are terrible threats, but they are growing pains that mark the birth of a global civilization.

In the end, the way to survive the Global MegaCrisis is to transform a way of life that no longer works. We are called to reinvent the rules, social institutions and concepts for understanding and governing our lives and societies. To simply recognize that consciousness forms the hard rock of reality would be a pivotal step in this existential crisis. Consciousness is the source of behavior itself, the cause of today's crises, and so that is also the source of potential solutions. By coming to grips with these threats we may – almost unwittingly – create a mature global order.

---

31    For hopeful signs of progressive change, see Ian Goldin, "The Second Renaissance" (*Nature*, Oct 18, 2017) and Gar Alpero-vitz, *Principles of Pluralist Commonwealth* (Washington, DC: The Democracy Collaborative, 2017)

32    Halal, "Through the MegaCrisis: The Passage to Global Maturity" (*Foresight,* 2013) Vol. 15 No. 5, pp. 392–404

# Box 1: Survey of TechCast Experts on Global MegaCrisis

**Decline to Disaster – 25% Probability** World fails to adjust. Climate shifts. Sea level rises. Energy shortages. Economic depression. Nuclear exchange. Civilization falls in some nations.

**Muddling Down – 35% Probability** Weak response. High-tech dark age. Ecological damage. Extreme weather. Increased poverty and conflict.

**Muddling Up – 28% Probability** World changes out of need and greater awareness along with more powerful technologies. Disaster avoided but some increase in disorder.

**Rise to Maturity – 12% Probability** Ideal transition to a responsible global order

---

The Pope thinks crisis opens an opportunity for existential change: "Where there is danger, there is always a saving power. That's the genius in the human story... When humankind has to act, it is precisely there in the threat itself; that's when the door opens."[33]

To put this challenge in perspective, we all pass through our personal crisis of maturity, usually rather well, and we should do the same for the global crisis. Try a mental shift by grasping the utter complexity of this historic passage and the many threats woven together into a Gordian Knot of incomparable complexity. Be sure to note the remarkable new powers of technology, as well as the aspirations of almost eight billion people striving to succeed. Then add impending transformations of business, government, education, medicine, religion and all other arenas of life – and you have the beginnings of a global consciousness.

The next chapter lays out the evidence for the coming synthesis of science and spirit to form the basis for an Age of Consciousness

---

33  "Pope Francis: A Crisis Reveals What Is in Our Hearts" (*New York Times,* Nov 26, 2020)

# CHAPTER THREE

# Uniting Science and Spirit: Technologies of Consciousness

The enormity of the question of consciousness was unexpectedly dropped into my lap when flying home from a business trip. My row companion was a Baptist pastor returning to his church in Washington. I told him who I was, and almost immediately he looked into my eyes and asked, "Are you saved? Have you accepted Jesus Christ as your Savior?" After he persisted in explaining the path to salvation, we exchanged views, and we agreed there are many paths.

This ordinary exchange nicely captures life's wondrous diversity of viewpoints and the enormous challenge of uniting our differences. It is emblematic of the countless similar islands of consciousness that meet in work, families and social functions. Life is lived moment to moment as our individual points of view intersect, sometimes productively and other times destructively. Consciousness pervades life – yet we have only a vague inkling of what it really is.

This chapter explains how consciousness forms the new frontier beyond information, knowledge and rational logic. There are two ways of explaining consciousness: 1) As a physical property of the brain, and 2) As a higher-order form of "human spirit." I summarize evidence from both sides of this debate, and then show that a synthesis of these views provides a richer and more powerful perspective. Finally, I show how "technologies of consciousness" are likely to enter mainstream use – not out of noble motives but out of sheer necessity.

## What Is Consciousness?

Consciousness is such a common part of life – like breathing air – that it is taken for granted. But with the Information Revolution, the study of consciousness has exploded into a central debate of our time. I am not a neuroscientist, although I am a seasoned scholar in the social sciences, knowledge and intelligence. As we will see soon, it's possible to integrate current understanding to reach useful conclusions.

To avoid getting lost in abstractions, let's look at examples of consciousness in action. Box 2 provides three accounts of people in conditions that alter consciousness, often dramatically.

These are vastly different experiences, but they all share a common element – a striking change in consciousness. The cleansing of grief, the flight of dance and the terror of war are all unique states of mind. There may be controversy over this rather mysterious phenomenon, but consciousness is very real and a central aspect of life.

## Box 2: Vignettes of Consciousness

**A woman crying over loss in her family** "I suddenly felt like a girl again after my parents' divorce. All at once, I was crying. It was as if I had an infected area where I had been stuffing my loss. I grieved openly and unashamedly for my mother and father, and for myself as a wife and a mother. This went on for 45 minutes. When it was over, I felt complete, cleansed, healed."

**A young girl dancing** "I didn't know him, and we started out tentatively. But soon we were making great loops around the room. It seemed that we weren't dancing at all; we were flying. We had risen a few inches off the floor, and we existed somewhere outside the law of gravity. The music, the other couples, and all else faded from thought as I danced in perfect joy and grace."

**A soldier's experience of war** "It is only now that I realize what a frightening experience I had been through. I was so completely wound up and braced for war that everything was taken in stride. Fear can be faced in the heat of battle if one subdues the emotions. But when it is over, then it is possible to emerge with full consciousness."

This reality of consciousness is fairly obvious, but the trouble occurs when trying to explain how it actually works. Scientifically, consciousness is the state of mind emerging from the brain. It's easy to understand perception, memory and other routine functions. But how do we direct attention? Evaluate options? Set goals? Who is doing the thinking?

The problem is more acute because we all experience life differently. Rather than sharing some fixed reality "out there," it is understood that individuals perceive the external world in their own personal way. Each mind is formed by different sensory perceptions, aspirations, traumatic experiences, imagination and countless other influences that produce wide mental differences, often in ways that seem incomprehensible to others. For example, abortion, gun control, the environment and other major issues resist rational solutions because they hinge on how we see the world – they are matters of consciousness.

Let's clarify with one of the notable pioneers in studying consciousness. Philosopher Rene Descartes charted the mind as a dualism between the physical world acting on the brain versus the spiritual world experienced by the soul. This distinction remains roughly valid today, although it is more useful to think of these differences as the "objective" and "subjective" aspects of consciousness. Figure 3 illustrates these two types of thought.[1]

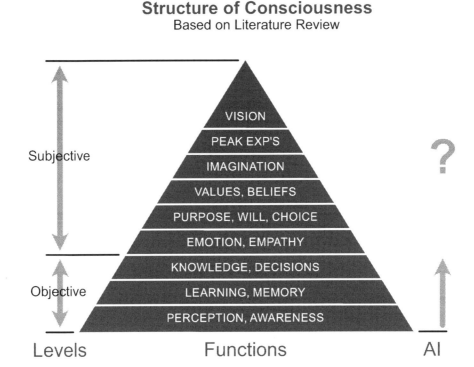

**Structure of Consciousness**
Based on Literature Review

**Figure 3**

The objective functions include perception, awareness, learning, memory, decisions, knowledge and other factual information. These are the rational foundations that built an orderly world. The subjective functions are inherently personal, or what scientists call "qualia." This includes emotions, will, purpose, beliefs, values, imagination, vision and other ethereal functions. Later in this chapter, I will introduce the concept of "human spirit" as a more convenient way think about this subjective realm.

The subjective level, or human spirit, is more powerful because it spans the higher-order functions that shape the objective level, as the many examples throughout this book demonstrate. For example, knowledge may influence subjective values, of

1    For authoritative works on consciousness, see Thomas Lombardo, *Future Consciousness: The Path to Purposeful Evolution* (Winchester, UK: Change Maker Books, 2017).

course, but people usually select knowledge that serves prior beliefs. Chapter One showed that people with strong political beliefs often reject factual knowledge, no matter how well authenticated. Even memory fails when the knowledge once held conflicts with existing views.

Rise a bit higher conceptually, and we see that the human spirit can transform entire lives far beyond the power of objective knowledge. Saul the Pharisee did not become Paul the Apostle because he learned new facts on the road to Damascus. He had a peak experience when a vision of God spoke to him, altering his consciousness irrevocably.

This famous story of St. Paul's conversion serves as a parable for the power of spiritual issues, values, beliefs and other subjective forms of thought. Paul's enormous influence in spreading Christianity through the world reminds that the force of human spirit can be relentless. It can overthrow rational logic and trigger dramatic life changes. Human spirit fundamentally establishes how we use knowledge.

> Consciousness is one of the great domains of the natural world, much like physical matter, energy and information. It encompasses all in its purview, including both good and bad. "Higher consciousness" and "global consciousness" are specific states in this domain. Higher consciousness, or higher-order consciousness, refers to the subjective functions that transcend objectivity. Global consciousness is defined later as a set of principles needed to create a sustainable world. These are all various forms of what I define as "human spirit."

Throughout this book, we will see many examples in which higher-order subjective functions change human consciousness. Satyan Linus Devados, Professor of Computer Science, outlined the importance of the subjective view:

> "The 21st Century grapples with basic themes of the humanities: gender and race, truth and power, Black Lives Matter, Me Too and fake news … These problems are not rocket science; they are far more difficult. Putting a man on the Moon is the easy stuff. The arts and humanities offer a different set of values needed for probing complexity."[2]

---

2    Devadoss, "A Math Problem Around Pi Day" (*Washington Post,* Jun 21, 2018)

While consciousness actually includes both levels, this book focuses on high-order subjective functions because that is the source of today's social disorder and the crux of resolving the challenges of maturity. And, as we saw in Chapter One, AI is automating the objective functions, forcing us more fully into the subjective realm beyond knowledge.

With this background in mind, we now turn to the contrast between scientific and spiritual theories of consciousness, which correspond to the objective and subjective aspects. Scientific approaches hold that consciousness lies in the physical brain, while a spiritual perspective points to the subjective level of human spirit. These two theories seem irreconcilable, although later we will see how they can be unified. But first, let's assess the support for both views.

## The Current Scientific View

Scientists are objective by the nature of their work, so they tend to be doubtful of spirituality.[3] Stephen Hawking expressed it this way: "I regard the brain as a computer... there is no heaven or afterlife; that is a fairy tale for people afraid of the dark."[4] Thought may be exceedingly complex from this view, but even free will, values, beliefs and everything we experience are thought to be a logical outcome of our "wet computer." Consider the views of scientists in Box 3:

These studies provide compelling evidence that some aspects of the mind are a result of genetic inheritance, brain chemistry and other physical causes. Nobel Laureate Francis Crick, co-discoverer of DNA, carries this logic to its conclusion: "Your joys, your sorrows, your sense of personal identity and free will, are no more than a vast assembly of nerve cells and their associated molecules."[5] This view holds that higher-order subjective thought can be explained by physical causes, proving there is no God-like "ghost in the machine."

---

3    Peter Lapatin, "What Scientists Believe" (*The New Atlantis: A Journal of Technology & Society,* Fall, 2010); Victor Stenger, "The God Issue" (*New Scientist,* Mar 12, 2012)

4    *The Guardian* (May 15, 2011)

5    Steven Pinker, *The Blank Slate,* Op. Cit.

# Box 3: Support for the Scientific View

**The Genetic Roots of Religion** Pulitzer Prize-winning scientist Edward Wilson founded the field of sociobiology to explain human behavior as inherited genetic traits. Wilson said: "Scientific knowledge holds that religious experience is entirely neurobiological."[6]

**Religiosity in the Brain** Studies demonstrate that spiritual experiences are traceable by PET scans to particular regions of the brain. Michael Persinger, a neuroscientist, concludes "Religion is a property of the brain and has little to do with what's out there."[7]

**Decisions Are an Illusion** Benjamin Libet, a physiologist, finds a one-third-second delay between the time an act is initiated in the brain and the time the subject reports a decision to initiate the act, suggesting that conscious decisions are a mere afterthought. But other scientists disagree.[8]

**Intuition Is Often Wrong** David Myers, psychologist at Hope College, thinks intuition is not a mystical sense but merely a subtle form of learning that is often wrong. Basketball players who think they are on a "hot streak," for instance, score no higher than they would ordinarily.[9]

**Out-of-Body Phenomena Explained** Olaf Blake, a neurologist, reports that mild electric currents to the brain cause out-of-body experiences. One subject said, "I am at the ceiling," and later "I'm back at the table now. What happened?"[10]

**No Free Will** Research of U. of Pennsylvania biologist Anthony Cashmore led him to conclude "free will is akin to religious beliefs, since neither complies with the laws of the physical world."[11]

From this perspective, it is only a small step to believe that advanced AI will soon exceed the power of human thought. This was reinforced when the IBM computer, Deep Blue, beat world chess masters in 1997 and again in 2003. The same logic anticipates a surreal future in which the human mind can be uploaded, stored and downloaded at will, like software.[12] I have a colleague who thinks it would be clever to email a spiritual epiphany or a sexual orgasm to someone.

There are even attempts to create an "artificial brain." Computer chips operating as artificial neurons in massive parallel networks can self-organize, learn and solve

---

6   Edward O. Wilson, *Sociobiology: The New Synthesis* (Belknap Press, 2000)

7   Carey Goldberg, "A Question of Will" (*Boston Globe,* Oct, 15, 2002)

8   Anil Ananthaswamy, "Free Will Is Not an Illusion" (*New Scientist,* Sep 23, 2010)

9   David Myers, *Intuition: Its Powers and Perils* (New Haven: Yale University Press, 2003),

10   Sherry Baker, "Ways to Leave the Body" (*Discover,* Jul 8, 2012)

11   John Horgan, "The God Experiments" (*Discover,* Jan 2006)

12   The concept of uploading the mind appeared in an academic journal: Ben Goertzel and Matthew Ikle, "Special Issue on Mind Uploading" (*International Journal of Machine Consciousness,* Jun 2012) Vol. 4, Issue 1

problems, as our minds do.[13] This must be scaled up dramatically to match the brain's 100 billion neurons interacting to create 100 trillion synapses, using only 0.00001 percent of the energy consumed by computers. But this is just a technical barrier, like deciphering the three billion bits of information in DNA. If science can break the DNA code, why not the brain?

All this evidence shows that science is doing a fine job of explaining the mechanisms of behavior. But beyond the mechanics, doubt arises out of the assumption that the mind is simply objective information. David Gelernter, professor of computer science, noted. "I don't know if there is a way to achieve consciousness other than living organisms … All we can discuss scientifically is objective knowledge. Consciousness is subjective."[14] Others may disagree, but the evidence in this chapter supports Gelernter's distinction.

That is the mystery. Where does subjectivity come from? When speaking to audiences, I often ask for a show of hands on this crucial issue – *Is there a fundamental difference between machine intelligence and human intelligence?* I invariably find that more than 90 percent think, "Yes, there is a fundamental difference." I have come to see that almost all people agree there is something special about the human mind. They may not be able to put their finger on it, but the current scientific model does not correspond with everyday experience.

The scientific explanations for religiosity and out-of-body experiences are probably valid but cause and effect could be confused. These spiritual effects seem to be activated by complex systems in the brain. But it may be more accurate to say that the brain serves independent spiritual purposes that we do not understand. Either way, we seem to be hard-wired for spirituality.

The famous biologist E.O. Wilson has shown that social behavior, such as tribalism, has been genetically built into humans by evolution, and the same seems to be true for spiritual behavior. In short, evolution seems to have endowed humans with spiritual abilities.[15] As all religions have claimed, we are essentially spiritual beings.

It is tempting to think this proves human thought surpasses machine intelligence, but could we be wrong? After all, people accepted for millennia the common belief that

---

13    Andreas Von Bubnoff, "A Brain Built from Atomic Switches Can Learn" (*quantamagazine,* Sep 20, 2017)

14    "Gelertner, Kurzweil Debate Machine Consciousness" (*Kurzweilai.com,* Dec 11, 2006)

15    E. O Wilson, *Sociobiology: The New Synthesis* (Cambridge: Harvard University Press, 1975)

the Earth is flat. Science is making great contributions by demonstrating that the mind can be modeled as a rational system, possibly leading to another historic revolution. Just as Copernicus shattered conviction in an Earth-centered universe and Darwin dispelled the distinction between humans and animals, neuroscience is challenging deeply held beliefs about the mind. But if we are little more than wet computers without free will – should we punish crime? Reward the successful? Believe in love?

## The Spiritual View

These difficulties lead to the spiritual view of consciousness. This does not involve supernatural beings, but simply recognizes the reality of the subjective state of mind, or "human spirit." Webster's dictionary defines human spirit as: "Will, consciousness, frame of mind, disposition, mood, as 'In high spirits.'" Think of the vignettes of grief, dance and war we saw earlier that portray the fluid, ethereal shifting of human spirit.

These higher-order mental functions "emerge" from the physical brain to take a non-physical life all their own. Nobel Laureate Roger Sperry thinks the mind acts as an independent force,[16] and the Dalai Lama claims this "luminous nature of awareness" transcends the brain.[17] Daniel Batson, a psychologist, put it best: "The brain is the hardware through which consciousness is experienced. To say the brain produces consciousness is like saying a piano produces music."[18]

From this view, human spirit is a distinctive phenomenon *beyond knowledge*. In fact, that's a good definition of human spirit or higher-order, subjective thought – *everything beyond knowledge*. Many scientists object to the term "spirit," but it is long past time to claim the legitimacy of human spirit as a scientific term. The evidence suggests there should be nothing controversial about this definition. Human spirit is apparent in everyday life; it can even be measured. As we shall see, it is empirical fact.

Adults are preoccupied with this subjective sphere because the crucial actions of life – succeeding in a career, making a marriage work, raising children – draw on moral purpose, mental strength and willpower. Try telling executives, parents and other

---

16   Sperry, R. W. "The Impact and Promise of the Cognitive Revolution," In R. W. Solso and D. W. Massaro (Eds.), *The Science of the Mind: 2001 and Beyond* (New York: Oxford University Press, 1995)

17   "On the Luminosity of Being" (*New Scientist*, May 24, 2003)

18   [17] Shankar Vedantam, "Tracing the Synapses of Spirituality" (*Washington Post*, Jun 17, 2001)

responsible persons that their actions are an "automatic response to stimuli" and you are likely to get a blank stare. To most people there is no need for proof – human spirit is self-evident. Box 4 shows abundant evidence on the spiritual side of this debate:

The data above suggest that human spirit exerts subtle but powerful influences over behavior. Health is affected by beliefs, friendships and optimistic or pessimistic states of mind. Prayer, meditation and other practices improve personal well-being and community spirit.

This prosaic human spirit is somewhat arbitrary and can change dramatically through scientific revolutions, nervous breakdowns, falling in love and religious conversions. The mind is continually shaped by a variety of forces: news events, ideas, drugs, meditation and prayer, psychotherapy, social rituals and ceremonies, art and music, dreams, weather and seasons, physical exercise and endless other causes. Almost anything can affect the mind, really. The "spiritual distillation" of all these experiences can be thought of as the "soul," a "personal cloud" that encapsulates our identity.

These mental shifts occur at the collective level as well as in individuals. Families, organizations, religious cults and even terrorist cells are usually held together by beliefs. Russia's collective soul went through a transformation when Marxist beliefs were overthrown for free markets.

Consciousness is so basic that it appears to energize all life forms. Animals use tools, have languages, create cultures and share a common consciousness, not fundamentally unlike humans. Plants sense elements in their environment, understand threats and make calculated responses to protect themselves – a rudimentary form of conscious intelligence. Even colonies of bacteria seem to be aware of their surroundings as they reach a "quorum" before deciding to act.[19]

Please do think this new frontier will be utopian. We know so little about spirituality that it is often dismissed as ignorance or fantasy. That's because its very nature involves belief systems that transcend logic. Consciousness is not always benign and can take almost any form. Dogmatic religiosity can be destructive, and it is easily misused by zealots. There will be no shortage of violence and war based on ideological conflict. We may even pit more intense moral differences against one another, creating biblical-like battles.

---

19    "Evidence Points to 'Metacognition' in Some Nonhuman Animals" (*Science Daily*, Sep 15, 2009)

# Box 4: Support for the Spiritual View

**Health Affected by Mind** Medical studies show people who feel in control, connected to others, and optimistic tend to be healthier and live longer. The well-known placebo effect is so strong that medical trials control for it, and the nocebo effect causes people who worry about sickness to become ill.[20]

**Power of Religion** Those practicing a religion live longer and are generally healthier, even after controlling for smoking, drinking and exercise. Dr. Jeff Levin at the National Institutes of Health reviewed the studies and found "The weight of evidence overwhelmingly confirms that spiritual life influences health."[21]

**Spirit and Community** Scientific studies demonstrate a link between meditation and social order. The ratio of people meditating is inversely related with crime and violence and directly related to positive behavior.[22]

**Valid Results in Parapsychology** A survey of extrasensory perception concluded the evidence is as strong as medical studies, but scientific bias prevents acceptance of this phenomenon. Meta-analyses of the literature showed that the beliefs of researchers are critical to results. One scientist said: "Some phenomena depend on beliefs."[23]

**Source of Creativity** Creative people are often mystified by the source of their inspiration. Famed author J.K. Rowling said, "It feels as if someone zapped the ideas into my head." Playwright Michael Frayn described it this way: "It came into my head instantaneously. I remember the moment very clearly," and novelist Saul Bellow said: "The book just came to me. All I had to do was catch it in buckets."[24]

**Near-Death Experiences** People who passed through near-death tell the same story of being welcomed by loved ones and religious figures. One saw intense light like "A mother's love only a million times stronger." Later they have no fear of death. Some have explained this as a function of the brain,[25] but others are unconvinced. Bruce Greyson, a psychiatrist, said "Brain chemistry does not explain this."[26] Dr. Sam Parnia practices resuscitation medicine and is convinced this is a "universal experience... something inexplicable with current science doesn't mean it is wrong."[27]

20    Gareth Cook, "The Nocebo Effect: How We Worry Ourselves Sick" (*newyorker*, Apr 3, 2013)

21    Jeff Levin, *God, Faith, and Health* (NY: Wiley, 2001)

22    Daniel Campos et al., "Exploring the Role of Meditation on Social Cognition" (*Frontiers of Psychology*, Apr 11, 2019)

23    Cardeña, E., "The Experimental Evidence for Parapsychological Phenomena" (*American Psychologist*, 2018) 73(5), 663–677; Daniel Engber, "Daryl Bem Proved ESP Is Real: Which Means Science is Broken" (*Slate*, Jun 7, 2017). U.S. and Russia devoted two decades to "remotely viewing" enemy activities, often with great success. One of the best psychics in the U.S program was first to identify the existence of Russia's Typhoon submarines.

24    "Saul Bellow" (*The Week*, Apr 22, 2005)

25    Kyla Hill, "The Death of 'Near Death" (*Scientific American*, Dec 3, 2012)

26    Charles Choi, "Peace of Mind" (*Scientific American*, Sep 12, 2011); Steven Kotler, "Extreme States," (*Discover*, Jul 2006); "On the Edge of the Known World" (*NewScientist*, Mar 13, 2004); Shankar Vedantan "Near Proof of Near Death" (*Washington Post*, Dec 17, 2001)

27    Brandon Keim, "Consciousness After Death" (*Wired*, Mar 24, 2013)

> Some type of belief system is unavoidable. Our goal should be to create more sophisticated belief systems that accord with the complexity of modern life.

Although the spiritual model makes sense intuitively, it also raises the question, Where does human spirit come from? I have no clear answer to this mystery, but it is possible that the mind is a manifestation of some "metaphysical spirit." A long tradition of scholarship in this area suggests we are connected through a form of 'spiritual energy" that permeates the universe.[28] Asian philosophers call it "chi," Westerners think of "the life force," and for the Catholic Church it is "grace." This does not necessarily imply divine powers. But we seem to be receptors and transmitters of this energy that gives life meaning and purpose. This universal spiritual energy may have its own laws, and we simply do not understand them. I know of no better explanation for the mystery of consciousness.

> Teilhard de Chardin noted the difficulty of accepting the revolutionary possibility of spiritual energy: "There is no concept more familiar to us than that of spiritual energy, yet there is none that is more opaque scientifically."[29]

In this view, the brain can be thought of as a vehicle for spiritual energy, constantly adapting in the struggle to find a trustworthy island of consciousness to see it through the sea of life. Each organism seems to be imbued with this energy, and these islands of consciousness aggregate into larger groups, forming entire social communities that develop a spirit all their own. All life past and present collectively could form the universal consciousness described by Carl Jung.[30]

This view also reveals how the forces driving civilization seem to originate in some higher form of spiritual energy flowing from the top of the Life Cycle of Evolution. It then cascades down like a waterfall through lower stages in the form of consciousness, knowledge, social behavior, and finally material artifacts. The Buddha noted: "With our thoughts, we make the world."

---

28    Willis Harman, *Global Mind Change* (Knowledge Systems, 1988)

29    Pierre Teilhard de Chardin, *The Phenomenon of Man* (New York: Harper, 1955)

30    Carl G. Jung, *The Red Book: Creation of a New Cosmology* (New York: W. W. Norton, 2009)

# A Synthesis of Science and Spirit

But the issue is hardly settled. Following controversy over a study showing that prayer affects the recipients, a Harvard researcher conducted a blind-study of 1800 patients who were prayed for. Finding no statistical differences, he concluded – "Case closed."[31] This reminds us that nothing beats reality. The universe is a very complicated place, and we are all engaged today in an historic social adventure to establish outposts in the frontier of consciousness.

The major problem seems to be confusion over evidence. Many think spirituality cannot be studied with scientific methods, while others feel it is self-evident. This was nicely stated in the Talmud: "For those who believe, no proof is necessary. For those who do not, no proof is possible." The challenge now is to reconcile these views.

The solution is to focus on those aspects of consciousness that are empirical. Leave aside the supernatural and concentrate on the very real phenomena of human spirit – the thoughts and behavior and that can be observed using scientific methods. These are empirical facts that psychologists, social scientists and anthropologists have studied for decades. Simply recognizing the legitimacy of the vast evidence in literature, humanities and liberal arts would amount to a scientific revolution. Prominent physical scientists know that science and spirit are compatible:[32]

**Freeman Dyson:** "Scientific materialism and religious transcendentalism are not incompatible. We have learned that matter is weird. It does not limit God's freedom."

**Max Plank:** "For religion, the idea of God is at the beginning; for science, the idea of God is at the end. Those who go deep enough to see the marvelous relationships among universal laws also recognize a creative power."

**Albert Einstein:** "The most beautiful and most profound emotion we can experience is the mystical. It is the source of all true science. Everyone who is seriously involved in science becomes convinced that some spirit is manifest in the laws of the universe."

---

31  Michael Shermer, Folk Science" (*Scientific American,* Aug 2006)

32  See Adam Engle, *The Universe in an Atom: Convergence of Spirituality and Science* (Morgan Road Books, 2005)

David Chalmers, an Australian cognitive scientist, thinks "We are likely to discover that consciousness is a fundamental property of the universe, like space, time and gravity."[33]

Quantum physics itself, the accepted paradigm in science, points directly to the role of consciousness. It has become a cliché to note that atomic particles do not settle into location until observed. In the terms of physics, the conscious process of measurement "collapses the probability spectrum" to produce reality.[34] Many speak of a new "second-order science" based on multiple observers who see different realities – what social scientists have been grappling with for decades.[35]

The new science of epigenetics also echoes this spiritual view. Rather than DNA being a fixed genetic code that determines behavior, it is now clear that experiences alter the expression of genetic traits, and the new behaviors are passed on to generations. Elizabeth Blackburn, who won the Nobel Prize, finds that the telomeres controlling life spans can be altered by attitudes. Traumatic experiences can ordinarily shorten life spans, but the damage can be offset if people treat the experience as a challenge rather than a burden.[36]

This synthesis of science and spirit could resolve the endless haggling over evolution. If scientists and creationists could stop shouting at each other, we might see that a broader paradigm can reconcile both views. The evidence supporting evolution is beyond dispute, but it merely explains the physical mechanisms involved. Conversely, a higher form of intelligence may guide evolution, but through God-like powers manifested in life forms rather than a biblical act of creation. Life seems energized by novel ideas plucked out of thin air and the endless tough choices that shape evolutionary acts, like selecting a mate. Endless little sparks of consciousness like these guide small steps that collectively may determine the course of evolution.

This synthesis may also explain why our "biogenetic universe" is hospitable to life. Rather than accept the possibility of some creative supernatural power, science now posits a "multiverse" in which our universe happens to be suited to life, while billions

33    Marc Kaufman, "A Meeting of Minds" (*Washington Post*, Sep 21, 2003)

34    Colin Jeffrey, "Experiment Suggests Reality Doesn't Exist Until It Is Measured" (*Science*, Jun 3, 2015)

35    Karl Muller, *Second-order Science* (Edition Echoraum, 2016)

36    Elizabeth Blackburn and Elissa Epel, *The Telomere Effect* (Grand Central Publishing, 2018)

of others remain sterile. Physicist Charles Townes noted the irony: "The speculation that there exist billions of invisible, parallel universes would be laughed out of town if it came from a religious text." Following the scientific principle of favoring the simplest theory (Occam's Razor), it would seem best to explore the possible existence of some form of spiritual energy than propose such convoluted explanations.

> Astronaut Edgar Mitchell put it best: "There are no unnatural or supernatural phenomena, only very large gaps in our knowledge of what is natural."[37]

Although subjective consciousness is self-evident to many, resistance is fierce because it eludes those fixated on a material view. Richard Dawkins, the biologist who achieved fame denying religiosity, participated in an experiment known to produce profound spiritual experiences. Dawkins reports he "didn't feel a thing." Contrast this with another scientist, Paul Ekman, who said upon meeting the Dalai Lama. "I was inexplicably suffused with a wonderful warmth throughout my body. It was palpable. I felt a goodness I'd never felt before in my life."

An interesting breakthrough suggests public opinion is shifting. Rupert Sheldrake, a biologist, has conducted experiments suggesting that energy fields guide conscious behavior. His studies show that learning occurs more easily after others have mastered the task, people can sense being stared at, dogs know when their masters are unexpectedly coming home.[38] When Sheldrake gave a TED talk on his research, skeptics objected that this was not science and should be dropped from the program. But the audience supported Sheldrake. Here's what a participant said:[39]

> "A tipping point has been reached. It's the first time I've ever seen the skeptics overwhelmed on a public forum. Information about consciousness research has spread far and wide, and its supporters are growing ever more vocal."

A century ago, who would have believed that moving images of people and all manner of knowledge would be transmitted through space and displayed on

---

37   Caspar Melville, "Natural History of the Soul" (*The Humanist*, Mar/Apr 2011)

38   "Rupert Sheldrake, *Seven Experiments that Could Change the World* (New York: Riverhead Books, 1995)

39   "The Debate About Rupert Sheldrake's Talk" (*blog. TED.com*, Mar 19, 2013)

smartphones? Yet we now know that the universe is alive with invisible radio-magnetic energy. One more step in this line of intellectual progress may carry science to a universe pulsing with spiritual energy.

For these reasons, science should recognize the possibility that a domain of consciousness may transcend the physical world. After all, doubt and uncertainty abound in quantum mechanics, the entanglement of atoms, the Big Bang, dark energy, the origins of life and other inexplicable phenomena. The dean of physics, John Wheeler, thinks "our observations might contribute to the creation of physical reality. We are shapers and creators living in a participatory universe."[40]

It may not be possible to know whether science will triumph and dispel belief in the soul, or spirit will gain ascendancy instead. Both should make advances over the next decades, and it is tempting to think they could converge in time. But for the foreseeable future, we seem to be propelled into a great controversy. Are humans simply biological systems for processing information? Or is there something about life that transcends knowledge? Will society be dominated by AI, the divine spark of life or a synthesis of the two? Whatever the outcome, we are about to witness a crucial scientific experiment that could produce fascinating results. Stay tuned.

## Mastering Consciousness

This is not simply an intellectual issue because a high-tech, globalizing world is raising the level of subjective consciousness. Culture is a sensitive barometer of values, and a Google search produces roughly the same huge number of hits for "mind," "spirit" and "soul" as for "food," "sex," and "housing." A scientific analysis of 600 million Twitter messages revealed the main things people want are "love, time, and good relationships."[41]

Regardless of whether we think of this in biological, digital, or spiritual terms, it would be a good idea to understand and guide this rise of consciousness. The spiritual model could gain ascendancy as it becomes increasingly clear that good health, strong communities, global order and other crucial aspects of life hinge on cultivating sound forms of consciousness.

---

40   Tim Folger, "Does the Universe Exist If We're Not Looking?" (*Discover*, Aug 14, 2002)

41   Anasse Bari et al., "What Do People Say They Want on Twitter? Love" (*Washington Post*, Dec 16, 2018)

One of our greatest challenges is to help people gain mastery over their increasingly difficult lives in an out-of-control world. All but saints struggle through a bewildering maze of information overload, complex relationships, bureaucratic institutions and sheer confusion over massive change. Stress is the basic cause of 75 to 90 percent of medical problems.[42] Many claim the biggest social problem today – crime, sexual promiscuity conflict, terrorism, depression, compulsive eating – stem from a culture of self-interest and other failures of spirit.

Spirituality may allow us to feel whole and experience bliss, but its practical function is alleviating the unusually troubling ills of our time. As I will show in Chapter Eight, we need some way to ease our turbulent lives, gain clarity and the moral will for tough decisions, maintain harmony with others and find some measure of peace and meaning in a confusing world.

That's why people are guiding their lives more skillfully through prayer, meditation, nature and a variety of other interventions for mastering that inner world. These are the technologies of consciousness (ToCs) that we use to change our state of mind. They may be thought of as tools, techniques or practices, but I like the term "technologies" because it highlights their power to shape consciousness. MIT geneticist Eric Lander said after working with the Dalai Lama: "We should regard Buddhism as a refined technology."

Consider the ebb and flow of your mind during a typical day. You wake and leave the dreamy haze of sleep, take a shower to refresh the senses, use coffee to stimulate attention for work, spring to action over a challenge, enjoy the relaxation of a drink before dinner and finally go off into sleep. In short, life's daily cycle is a sequence of small but important changes in consciousness aided by ToCs – hot showers, coffee, action, alcohol, sleep.

The idea of using ToCs to change the mind may appear daunting, and possibly disturbing. That's why Chapter Eight provides detailed examples of three main ToCs in use – meditation, nature, and psychotropic drugs – moving society toward an Age of Consciousness.

A useful example comes from my garden. One day, I was inspired to build a gazebo in a secluded corner. The design came to me in a flash, and I built it myself. When

---

42    Joe Robinson, "Three-Quarters of Your Doctor Bills Are Because of Stress" (*Huffington Post*, Jul 22, 2013)

guests visit, I take them through the garden to the gazebo, and they are always amazed. Then a calm serenity takes over as the special mood of the place sinks in. I've come to think of the gazebo as a "mind machine" because I can count on its ability to create this calming sensation. That is the power of technology to shape consciousness.

# CHAPTER FOUR

# Democratic Enterprise: Collaboration Between Business and Society

While in Moscow shortly after the Berlin Wall came down, I was struck by an eerie similarity between the ideologies of capitalism and communism. My Western colleagues were berating the Russians for their rigid views on central planning when it occurred to me that Americans are no less ideological, but in more subtle ways. Where Marxism is out of touch with economic reality, a closer look in the next few pages will show that American business is so skewed by its focus on money that we often miss the debilitating social realities that plague the West.

This chapter explores how business is moving beyond its traditional focus on profits to a human-centric model that serves both social interests and financial needs. Corporations are the most powerful institutions in the world, so this shift in economic consciousness could be revolutionary.

Corporate leaders are already shaping this transition. After showing how the American business model has led to economic and social crises, I summarize examples from the leading edge to illustrate the coming of "democratic enterprise." We also see that AI is driving a new class of creative work that is human-centered. Jobs are changing at all levels, from CEOs to employees.

## The Irony: American Capitalism is Bad Economics

The USSR collapsed because central planning could not cope with the exploding complexity of the information revolution, and this fundamental flaw brought down communism. The West was fortunate to have a self-correcting market system, but markets can vary enormously. The Japanese practice a collective form of business that serves society; Europeans favor worker participation; the Nordic nations form civic associations; and China has state capitalism.

In contrast, the US has traditionally favored a form of capitalism that places profits above workers, customers, the public, the environment and other social interests. The result is the well-known problems of inequality, low wages, economic crises, unstable jobs, failing infrastructure, climate change and the other social ills of our time. This problem is so severe that an article in the *Harvard Business Review* compared the American economy to the dire predictions of Karl Marx and found that many of them had proven valid.[1]

---

1   Umair Haque, "Was Marx Right?" (*Harvard Business Review,* Sep 7, 2011)

This old reliance on the "invisible hand" of economics to form "perfect markets" that "efficiently serve all social interests" is a beautiful theory. But it has its limitations.[2] American CEOs typically earn roughly 500 times their average worker's pay, and the top one percent of the population own more wealth than the entire bottom 90 percent.[3] In 2019, after years of concern over gross inequality, corporate CEOs' pay rose 18 percent/year to an average of almost $19 million/year, for a total 940-percent increase since 1978. Meanwhile, worker pay was basically unchanged.[4] One CEO received $786 million.[5] In contrast, the US has the greatest share of low-wage jobs in the modern world, with the bottom 20 percent living in poverty.[6]

During the 2020 pandemic, while most Americans were struggling with unemployment, billionaires gained US$1 trillion, which went largely to Jeff Bezos and Elon Musk. The gains of these two men were greater than the GDPs of 139 countries.[7]

A RAND study summed up the problem. Average American workers would be receiving $100,000 per year instead of $50,000 today if normal distribution rates had remained in effect during the past few decades. All told, business moved roughly $50 trillion from the middle class to the top one percent of society – "The Great Wealth Transfer."[8] For the bulk of US workers, Marx's critique about the "immiseration of the working class" does not seem far off.

In one of history's great ironies, many children of the super-rich are ashamed of all this inherited wealth and they dislike the capitalist system that produced such inequality. One 28-year-old who inherited $30 million says, "I want to build a world where someone like me, who controls tens of millions, is impossible." A young heiress had much the same attitude, "The money I'm living on was made by exploiting people."[9]

2 "Capitalism Redefined" (*Democracy*, Winter, 2014)

3 "Nation's Top 1 Percent Now Have Greater Wealth Than the Bottom 90 Percent" (*Seattle Times*, Dec 8, 2017)

4 Jeff Stein and Jena McGregor, "Annual Pay Surges for CEOS but Not Their Employees" (*Washington Post*, Aug 17, 2018); Jena McGregor, "CEO group shifts view on maximizing profits" (*Washington Post*, Aug 20, 2019)

5 Steven Pearlstein, "The Confounding $786 Million Question: Does Anyone Deserve Such a Paycheck?" (*Washington Post*, Jan 6, 2019); Tyler Kepner and Kevin Draper, "Mike Trout Received a Huge Payday. But Others Still Dwarf Him" (*New York Times*, Mar 19, 2019)

6 Harold Meyerson, "Low Wages Aren't Working" (*Washington Post*, Sep 20, 2013)

7 Christopher Ingraham, "World's Richest Men Add Billions as Others Struggle" (*Washington Post*, Jan 2, 2021)

8 Carter C. Price and Kathryn Edwards, "Trends in Income From 1975 to 2018" (*Rand*, Nov 20, 2020)

9 Zoe Beery, "The Rich Kids Who Want to Tear Down Capitalism" (*New York Times*, Nov 27, 2020)

Beyond the economics, the inhumanity of a system devoted to money brutalizes both those at the bottom and those at the top. While the suffering of the poor is obvious, the toll on the wealthy can also be serious. Studies show that wealthy people are less likely to show understanding and compassion, leaving them lacking the very traits of emotional intelligence needed to cope in a complex world.[10] And all suffer from stress and its drain on health, resulting in mental health problems like depression, narcissism and schizophrenia.[11] This high-pressure work environment has been shown to increase medical care costs, turnover, absenteeism, and accidents, draining $500 billion from the US economy annually.[12]

> Professor Jeffrey Pfeffer of the Stanford Business School summed up the problem:
>
> "Today's stressful work conditions are harming company performance and individual well-being, and this needs to be the clarion call to stop. There is too much damage being done."[13]

In the final analysis, the irony is that this profit-centered system is not only wanting in human terms, it also is bad economics. Inequality *decreased* US GDP by five percent cumulatively over the past two decades.[14] Rankings of global competitiveness show that leading social democracies (Switzerland, Singapore, Netherlands, Germany, Hong Kong, UK, Sweden, Japan, Finland, Norway, Denmark, New Zealand, Canada, Israel)[15] often beat the US in economic performance. They also provide their citizens with benefits Americans can only wish for – universal health care, childcare, quality education, financial security and a generally higher quality of life. These competitive nations also rank at the top of the UN happiness ratings.[16]

The basic problem is that the profit motive is deeply ingrained in American culture. Ask almost any adult in the US about the purpose of business, and you are likely to get

10    Daisy Grewal, "How Wealth Reduces Compassion" (*Scientific American*, Apr 10, 2012)

11    Richard Wilkinson and Kate Pickett, *The Inner Level: How More Equal Societies Reduce Stress, Restore Sanity and Improve Everyone's Well-Being* (Random House/Penguin Press, 2018)

12    Emma Seppalal and Kim Cameron, "Proof That Positive Work Cultures are More Productive" (*Harvard Business Review*, Dec 1, 2015)

13    Jeffrey Pfeffer, *Dying for a Paycheck* (Boston: Harvard Business, 2017)

14    Thomas Piketty, *Capital in the Twenty-First Century* (Cambridge, MA.: Belnap Press of Harvard University, 2014)

15    Klaus Schwab, *The Global Competitive Index 2017-2018* (World Economic Forum, 2018)

16    John F. Helliwell, Richard Layard and Jeffrey Sachs, *The World Happiness Report 2019* (United Nations, 2019)

the same answer – "To make money." But contrast this with the attitudes of the young: a recent survey found that 87 percent of young Americans said corporations should do more than just make money, and a majority now favor socialism.[17] The young may not be clear on what kind of economic system they have in mind, but they do know it should serve social needs primarily.

Please do not mistake this critique as an attack on business. I am a business owner myself (TechCast), and I know the struggle to survive in a competitive world. But I also know that the profit-centered form of business is outmoded in an age *beyond knowledge*. Yes, the US enjoys vibrant entrepreneurial freedom, and it has led the world in innovation (Silicon Valley, for example.) and sheer market size. But the single-minded focus on money that fueled the industrial past no longer makes sense when the most critical resources have shifted from factories, industrial machines, and other forms of material capital to the knowledge, innovation, human intelligence and creativity required to solve huge social challenges ahead.

## Learning from the Leading Edge of Business

Recent events stress that a human-centered form of business is emerging beyond profit to include all interests. Here are some telling statements from authoritative business leaders:

**Laurence D. Fink, founder and chief executive of BlackRock**, which holds US$6 trillion in investments, sent this statement to 1000 of the world's largest corporations:[18]

> "Society is demanding that companies… serve a social purpose… To prosper over time, every company must not only deliver financial performance but also show how it makes a positive contribution to society."

**Jeffrey Sonnenfeld, a dean at the Yale School of Management,** said of Fink's statement,

---

17   Tim Wilson, "How Corporations Can Be a Force for Good" (*Washington Post*, Sep 29, 2017)

18   Andrew Ross Sorkin, "BlackRock's Message: Contribute to Society or Risk Losing Our Support" (*New York Times*, Jan 15, 2018)

"It is huge for an institutional investor to take this position across its portfolio… I've never seen anything like it."

**Alan Murray, chief editor of *Fortune* magazine**, noted a critical change:[19]

"… business leaders believe they must take up the mantle … to address social problems … Companies are moving beyond fuzzy notions like sustainability and corporate citizenship to making meaningful social impact central to how they compete."

Note that these comments are not from liberal activists but from business leaders concerned about income inequality, climate change, job losses and other mounting social crises. Soon after, the Business Roundtable issued a statement ending the primary importance of shareholders and acknowledging the equally important roles of stakeholders.[20] If done well, this broader role should go beyond traditional ideas of social responsibility to increase value for all groups, including profitability for shareholders.

This is but a small step in the right direction. Yet, it may mark a passage that could be truly revolutionary. By recognizing the economic reality that all stakeholders are essential to business success, corporations could become engines of social progress as well as financial gain.[21] This move to a human-centric model of enterprise would be roughly comparable to the shift from an Earth-centric view of the universe to Copernicus's understanding that planets revolve around the Sun. It should be nothing less than a major shift in economic consciousness.

> Studies confirm that having women in corporate leadership improves business performance, largely because women excel at forming effective working relationships.[22]

19    Alan Murray (*Fortune*, Sep 1, 2016)

20    "Business Roundtable Redefines the Purpose of a Corporation to Promote 'An Economy That Serves All Americans'" (*Business Roundtable press release*, Aug 19, 2019)

21    See Amy Bernstein, "Shareholder Wealth vs. Stakeholder Health," (*Harvard Business Review*, Apr 24, 2017)

22    "When Women Take Over Family Firms, Profitability Increases," (*Harvard Business Review*, Mar 17, 2014)

To put this in perspective, consider the three models in the figure below. The profit-centered model is most familiar, while corporate social responsibility (CSR) has tried to shift the focus to stakeholders over the past decades, without much success. The problem is that CSR is the mirror opposite of the profit model, and it ignores the need for profitability. Attempts to implement CSR failed often because well-meaning managers were simply being philanthropic, leading many to think an alternative to profit-centered capitalism is not possible.[23]

In contrast, the collaborative enterprise model goes beyond CSR to form a more productive system that benefits all interests, including making more money for shareholders. It can be a competitive advantage. This more realistic "theory of the firm" allows managers to move beyond the bottom line. They can transcend self-interest to focus on the collective interests of society while also meeting capitalism's traditional goal.

> Studies by the premier consulting firm, McKinsey, conclude, "shares of companies that connect effectively with all stakeholders outperform competitors by two percent per year on average."[24]

My studies show that the social interests in any business – workers, customers, partners and the public – are roughly similar to the role of investors. All these groups invest resources, incur costs and gain benefits, much like investors. Any enterprise is basically a socio-economic system composed of key stakeholders that perform crucial functions. Focusing exclusively on capital sub-optimizes the entire system. From a more realistic view, the obvious need is to integrate all these resources into a more productive whole.[25] That is what any good executive must do to build a viable enterprise. Here's how Bonville Power harnessed the knowledge of its stakeholders:

> "We used to treat outsiders (labor unions, the public, regulators) as a nuisance. After working with them, our adversaries helped us find creative solutions to intractable problems. Public involvement is a must for today's managers. Conflict is unavoidable; the only choice is whether to dodge it or harness it."

23 For instance, James O'Toole records the many failures in his book, *The Enlightened Capitalists* (Harper Business, 2019)

24 Sven Smit, "Why Business Needs to Strike a New Deal with Society" (*McKinsey,* Apr 23, 2018)

25 Halal, "The Collaborative Enterprise: A Stakeholder Model Uniting Profitability and Responsibility" (*Journal of Corporate Citizenship,* Summer 2001)

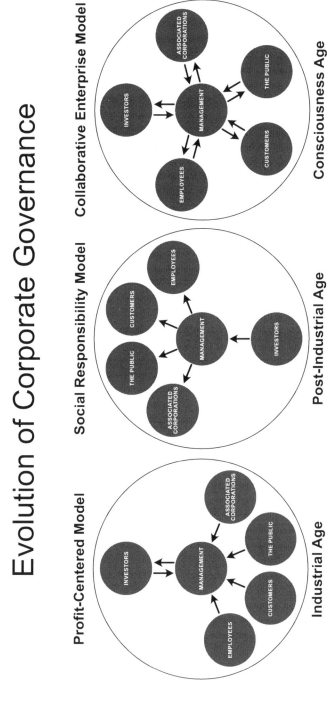

**Figure 4**

These concepts are now practiced among progressive companies and taught at business schools around the world. Recent surveys show that only five percent of

CEOs now say they are "mainly focused on profits." Other studies find that business leaders think stakeholder collaboration improves financial gains and serves society better.[26] And because working with stakeholders strengthens these critical relations, it can even reduce risk.[27] Consider some examples in Box 6 below:

## Box 6: Exemplars of Democratic Enterprise

**Whole Foods** has thrived under a philosophy that holds, "Profits are a by-product of treating people well, not the top priority." Employees work in teams that manage themselves, hire co-workers, select products, and get bonuses for good work.

**Starbucks** embraced the community model of governance when its CEO, Howard Schultz, turned employees and other groups into collaborating stakeholders.

**Nucor** is one of the world's most successful steel firms because each mill team builds a cohesive culture based on performance and collaboration. Top workers earn three times the industry average, and the CEO said of Nucor: "Our culture outperforms anything."

**Johnson & Johnson** continues to garner respect by requiring its 80 small businesses to be self-managed. Each unit has its own governing board and focuses on the needs of the doctors, nurses and patients who use its products.

**KKR,** once hated for its leveraged buyouts, is giving employees shares in the companies it controls. One client company, Gardner Denver, gave 6,000 employees $100 million of stock. As its chairman, Pete Stavros, said, "treating employees like business partners can create value."

**IKEA** has become a household name by providing low-priced high-quality furniture. The company cooperates with suppliers and babysits shoppers' children, and executives periodically work registers in the stores.

**Unilever** has become a global powerhouse by helping to cure poverty, clean water and alleviate climate change. The CEO said "You can't ignore your impact on society. In the future, this will be the only way to do business."

**Nortel** has worked to integrate profits and responsibility. The CEO noted: "Stakeholder collaboration shows a direct correlation between financial results, customer satisfaction and employee well-being."

**The Tata Group** in India is a global competitor that provides employees health care and education in its own hospitals and schools. The CEO says, "Tata will not grow over dead bodies."

**The UN Global Compact** is an association of businesses committed to human rights, labor, environment and anti-corruption. It includes over 13,000 organizations from more than 145 countries.

**B Corporations** include over 2,000 companies across 50 countries that meet standards of social and environmental goals and stakeholder interests.

**Business for Social Responsibility** is a global network of 250+ companies, thought leaders, and stakeholders that share best practices and forges relationships for innovative solutions. Also see the work of Hazel Henderson on creating ethical markets and economic systems.

26    Ken Favaro, "What's the Link Between Strategy and Doing Good?" (*Strategy-Business*, Sep 3, 2019)

27    "What Americans Want From Corporations" (*Just Capital*, Sep 21, 2020), "The Case for Stakeholder Capitalism" (*McKinsey*, Nov 12, 2020)

But could this human focus degenerate into an unsustainable form of philanthropy? The key to success is to *form collaborative stakeholder partnerships that solve strategic problems and create added value.* In the end, any viable enterprise must be productive to survive in a competitive marketplace.[28] Employees, customers, the public and partners provide valuable resources (labor, purchasing power, infrastructure, supply chains). They also provide knowledge and commitment in return for social benefits, while the corporation gains profits and reduces risk. Business leaders can then be relieved of their old role as simply money makers and become servant leaders concerned for the corporate community. My surveys of hundreds of managers show that more than 80 percent favor stakeholder collaboration.

## The Robots Are Coming – to Make You Creative

Not only is business working with stakeholders, the rise of AI is also pushing work towards this same economic consciousness. As AI increasingly automates work, transforms industries and society itself, there is a gripping fear that "The robots are coming to take your jobs!" Roughly half of present jobs could be lost to automation – even professional work is vulnerable – possibly leading to mass unemployment. But this transition offers great opportunities for a new wave of creativity and a more human-centered form of work.

A TechCast study estimated changes in future employment patterns.[29] Results are tabulated below and show that automation is likely to eliminate about 20 percent of routine jobs by 2030, but the loss is likely to be compensated by roughly 11 percent of workers finding new jobs in "creative work." Another roughly 8 percent would gain a Guaranteed Minimum Income (GMI), also known as Universal Basic Income (UBI). This "muddling through" scenario could keep global unemployment at not much higher than the ten-percent level.

This trend follows a well-worn historic path. Automation steadily replaced most manual labor in farming, then in manufacturing, and now it promises to automate services and knowledge work. What we have learned is that automation eliminates routine tasks that can be relegated to machines, freeing people to focus on more difficult tasks that can only be handled by humans. I suspect the same will prove true for the automation of knowledge. We simply cannot yet see the opportunities that will appear on this new frontier. Futurist Ray Kurzweil explained: "You can't describe the new jobs because they're in industries that don't exist yet."[30]

---

28  Tracey Keys et al., "Making the Most of Corporate Social Responsibility" (*McKinsey Quarterly*, Dec 2009)

29  Halal et al., "Forecasts of AI and Future Jobs in 2030" (*Journal of Futures Studies*, Dec 2016) 21(2) 83–96

30  "Why Futurist Ray Kurzweil Isn't Worried About Technology Stealing Your Job" (*KurzweilAI*, Sep 27, 2017)

**Table 2**
**Expert Survey Results for OECD Nations in 2030**
**Number of respondents = 53**

| Job Category | 2020 (Background Data) | 2030 (Expert Forecasts) | 2030 - 2020 |
|---|---|---|---|
| **Complex Manual Work** <br> Barbers, janitors, farmers, cleaners, cooks, gardeners, repairmen, carpenters, dentists, care givers | 19 % | 18 % | -1 % |
| **Routine Work** <br> Well-structured manual and service tasks easy to automate: factory work, clerical jobs, driving trucks, etc. | 35 | 17 | -18 |
| **Service/Knowledge Work** <br> Teaching, law, medicine, management, the arts and other professional work likely to be transformed rather than automated. | 34 | 31 | - 3 |
| **Creative Work** <br> Leadership, entrepreneurship, innovation, collaboration, strategy, vision, etc. The next frontier beyond knowledge. | 4 | 15 | + 11 |
| **GMI** <br> (Guaranteed Minimum Income, or Universal Basic Income - UBI) | 0 | 8 | + 8 |
| Unemployment | 8 | 11 | + 3 |
| **TOTAL** | 100% | 100% | 0% |

The solution is to recognize that AI can automate routine knowledge work, but there exists an economic domain *beyond knowledge* – creativity, entrepreneurship, vision, collaboration, marketing, supervision, imagination, wisdom and other higher-order functions.[31] That accords with studies showing a gradual increase in human intelligence of three IQ points per decade.

> Jack Ma, founder of China's Alibaba, said: "Technology will never replace humans. People will always surpass machines because we possess wisdom."[32] Philosopher Sean Kelly claims "Nothing but a human being can properly be understood as a genuinely creative genius."[33]

Intelligent machines may take over routine service and knowledge tasks, but the technology will remain limited, and people will always want a real person to provide human contact and handle tough issues. Staff is growing rapidly in universities, hospitals, research institutes, and other advanced settings for these reasons. The service and knowledge work sector could grow dramatically in the years to come.

This positive scenario could fail, obviously, permitting the "High-Tech Dark Age" noted in Chapter Two to dominate instead. In this case, the logic of technology would rule, autocratic leaders would govern, and people would be forced accept the harsh demands of raw capitalism. There are probably many other possibilities as well. The outcome hinges on consciousness, and trends noted throughout this book suggest we should see a vast increase in higher consciousness. The widespread use of AI alone is likely to increase our collective knowledge and intelligence to unprecedented levels.

In the end, rather than diminishing people, the net effect of AI may be to enhance these talents that are unique to humanity. This may seem contrary to many who are convinced a disaster looms ahead. We respectfully suggest that, yes, the robots are coming to take your jobs. But this offers endless opportunities for creative work that can foster a more innovative, prosperous and thoughtful civilization. As always, it depends on mastering consciousness.

Now let's turn to the big question, How can business leaders make this shift to democratic enterprise?

---

31    Howard Yu, "Human Creativity in the Age of Smart Machines" (*Strategy + Business*, Nov 8, 2018)

32    Shea Driscoll, "Technology Will Never Replace Humans" (*South China Morning Post*, Oct 12, 2017)

33    "A Philosopher Argues That AI Can't Be an Artist" (*Technology Review*, Feb 21, 2019)

# Business Leaders May Become Society's Heroes

Despite growing attention to these ideas, cooperation is only used marginally in the US. The past 40 years of Reaganomics unleashed the power of individualism and competition. Now the crucial challenge is to foster collaborative working relationships. That's why progressive managers have long practiced "coopetition" – cooperating even with competitors to produce better results for all. That's also why corporate partnerships have grown to the highest level of this century.[34] Social responsibility and ethics are commendable, but it takes active collaboration to resolve tough challenges and create value.

> The former CEO of Michelin and new chairman of Renault-Nissan-Mitsubishi alliance noted: "If you have a purpose that includes a well-considered level of social and environmental responsibility, you're going to increase profits in the long run."[35]

Critics may dismiss this as socialism, but corporate leaders choose to do this without government intrusion, so it's really enlightened free enterprise. The concept could also be viewed as a form of "economic democracy," a "corporate community," "human enterprise," or "a better way to make money." Terms like "conscious capitalism" are not accurate because the new system would no longer based primarily on capital but on the social resources of stakeholders. That's why I use the terms "collaborative enterprise" and "democratic enterprise."

The impacts of such an historic change are so vast they defy exhaustive analysis, but a few advantages stand out. The dominance of money would yield to more balanced policies that include the human dimension, and this would soften the harsh features of markets while also enhancing innovation and productivity. Cooperation could provide a form of self-regulation to avoid hobbling business with excessive controls, relieving governments of much of their responsibility for the public good.[36]

---

34    Bob Saada and Benjamin Gomes-Casseres, "Why Your Next Deal May Be a Partnership" (*Strategy n+ Business*, Dec 3, 2018)

35    Jeffrey Rothfeder, "Rolling Toward Responsible Capitalism" (*Thought Leaders*, May 17, 2019)

36    Steven Pearlstein, *Can Capitalism Survive? Why Greed Is Not Good* (New York: St. Martin's Press, 2018)

An important change would be that business leaders could assume their rightful place as social heroes instead of pariahs. After all, what is the point of striving for millions of dollars each year? Numerous studies show that happiness peaks at around $75,000 per year, and the rest is simply ego enhancing. Instead, this is a great opportunity for managers to take the lead, and thereby benefit their companies and the world. As a side benefit, business leaders could improve both their reputations and their personal satisfaction.

I was fortunate to witness a collaborative CEO in action when visiting a large company. At the conference table were managers, union officials, suppliers, distributors, advertisers and local government leaders. The CEO did not seem an imposing person, and I wondered how he managed to hold this group of big egos together.

It soon became clear this was a different type of leader. The CEO was intent on seeing others offer their ideas and rarely spoke himself. What was most remarkable is that he listened carefully. What a breath of fresh air! A leader who really cares what people think? Who wants to hear the messy truth? Surely this was a facade, I thought.

But it energized the group. People brought out their problems, ideas and other agendas normally hidden from view. The CEO simply asked an occasional question and clarified what was happening. But the group controlled the meeting. And their control affirmed that this was *their* organization. This corporate community held a diversity of valuable resources to be managed by them collectively. They were responsible for success, and they had to make it work.

Watching this man, I learned the essence of real leadership is humility.[37] Beneath this humble appearance, he was accorded deep respect. Not because of his power, but precisely because he yielded his authority to the group. They would do things for this man that no ordinary boss could even ask for. By giving up formal power, he actually gained the greater power of servant leaders.

True, this type of leadership is limited to a small segment of progressive organizations. Profit is an obvious business goal, directly measured, and pressure from Wall Street is relentless, leaving most organizations focused on quarterly gains.

---

37    For instance, see James Collins, *Good to Great* (Glasgow: William Collins, 2001)

Companies seem to be trapped in their financial statements, roughly as the Soviet apparatchiks of old were trapped in their five-year plans.

The greatest force for change is the recognition among creative business leaders that combining profit and social needs is not only possible but also a competitive necessity. Here's how Microsoft's CEO, Satya Nadella, described it: "We don't have a long-term business if we don't address the inequities." And Nick Hanauer, a self-described plutocrat, warned "If we don't do something to fix the glaring inequalities, the pitchforks are going to come for us."[38]

The US founded modern democracy, so Americans should be the most natural source of leadership in developing this second democratic revolution. But the US may be so committed to raw capitalism that other nations could take the lead.

I have a modest suggestion to help spur my countrymen along. In the tradition of liberation movements that freed slaves, women and ethnic minorities, we should encourage business leaders to reclaim their freedom and humanity for the good of their organizations, their nations, the world and their souls. To liberate American businesspeople from their financial shackles, I therefore issue a call to *Free the Fortune 500!*

---

38    Nick Hanauer, "The Pitchforks Are Coming – For Us Plutocrats" (*Politico*, July 15, 2014)

# CHAPTER FIVE

# A New Social Contract: Centrist Politics and Government Markets

After more than 200 years of struggle building modern democracies, who would have thought autocrats could sweep popular rule away so easily? As of 2021, China, Russia, Poland, Hungary, Austria, Turkey, Egypt, the Philippines, Venezuela, Brazil and most of the Middle East live under strongman rule, state controls, muzzled media, isolationism and harassing opponents. Freedom House notes this is the 15th consecutive year of declining global freedom.[1]

China's powerful example is most compelling. This unique blend of market capitalism and state control has in many ways outrun liberal democracies and leapt ahead of the West in just a few decades. The data from China is inaccurate sometimes, but the country seems to lead the world in home ownership, Internet use, college graduates, solar cells and more.[2] Admiration for the Chinese model is reminiscent of the 1960s, when many thought the Soviet Union's efficient form of central planning was superior to the messy nature of capitalism and democracy.

People did not see the resolution ahead when the Soviet Union collapsed in 1990. Something similar seems likely about strongman rule. Today's autocracies could be overthrown by solving the problems that plague democracy. This chapter will show that the conflict between left and right could be turned into powerful centrist solutions, and that governments could be revived by creating managed markets for public services.

This seems a formidable challenge, almost impossible, but that is exactly what big shifts in consciousness can do. The failure of both conservatives and liberals to resolve the MegaCrisis opens a frontier for progressive political leaders to shape a "politics of cooperation" able to unite nations in a rejuvenated common purpose.

## The Decline of Democracy and the Rise of Homo Sovietus

Start with the damaging instability in capitalist markets. We had the collapse of Asian economies in 1997, the dot.com crash in 2000, the Great Recession of 2008, and the pandemic recession is underway as this book goes to press. These destructive cycles have destroyed millions of lives and trillions of dollars, and they leave serious doubts about today's "casino capitalism."

---

1    Max Boot, "Freedom Is Declining" (*Washington Post*, Mar, 2020)

2    Andrew Sullivan, "Trump's First Year Has Been a Disaster: Here's Why I Have Hope" (*New York Times*, Jan 5, 2018)

Many blame a culture of rampant consumerism, speculation and marketing hype.[3] Strong vocal groups lobbying for special interests have polarized electorates and frozen governments in gridlock. The mercurial nature of a hyper-connected public hooked on the power of social media, the sheer size of government bureaucracies, and the corrupting effects of money on politicians have driven people into the hands of demagogues.

These are valid problems, but the fundamental issue is that democracy itself is failing in critical ways. The US Congress has failed to act on policies approved by strong 70- to 80-percent majorities: universal health care, reasonable gun controls, paid parental leave, higher minimum wages, wide access to abortion, legal marijuana and many other issues. In a study of 1,779 policies over the past two decades, the authors conclude, "…average Americans appear to have a minuscule, near-zero, insignificant impact on public policy."[4]

> A Harvard Business School study concluded: "We believe Trump's election is a sign of a fundamentally deep dissatisfaction… America's political system is an obstruction to economic growth and the single most important problem facing the country."[5]

The problem shows up clearly in performance data. The US ranks near the bottom of 36 developed nations in health care, education, renewable energy, infrastructure, childcare, life expectancy and voter turnout. Americans also have among the highest levels of poverty, obesity, guns per capita, violence and child mortality.[6] The top 10 percent of the country earns three times as much as the bottom 90 percent, and the top 0.1 percent alone earns as much as the entire bottom 90 percent.[7] Ironically, this disparity is roughly similar to Russia, where the wealth of a handful of oligarchs, including Vladimir Putin, is as great as total household assets across the nation.[8] Harvard strategist Michael Porter concludes, "It's like we're a developing country."[9]

3    David Von Drehle, "When the Internet Turns Against Democracy" (*Washington Post*, Jun 24, 2018); Kurt Andersen, *Fantasyland: How American Went Haywire* (New York: Random House, 2017)

4    Yascha Mounk, "America Is Not a Democracy" (*Atlantic*, Mar 2018)

5    Jeffrey Sparshott, "Harvard Business School's Latest Study Looks at American Politics and Finds a Rigged System" (*Wall Street Journal*, Sep 13, 2017)

6    Yoni Applebaum, "Is the American Idea Over?" (*Atlantic*, Nov 2017)

7    Matthew Stewart, "The Birth of a New American" (*Atlantic*, Jun 2018)

8    David von Drehle, "This is the Moment to Stand Up to Putin" (*Washington Post*, Jul 15, 2018)

9    Max Boot, "A Lesson in Our Backwardness" (*Washington Post*, Dec 29, 2020)

The US spends more on defense than the next several largest nations combined, yet it has among the lowest social benefits and quality of life. Freedom is wonderful, but the national cache of guns far exceeds those of all other nations per capita, producing an equivalently disproportionate number of mass shootings, homicides, suicides and other deaths, a toll far greater than that of foreign terrorism.[10] JP Morgan's CEO, Jamie Dimon, said, "It's embarrassing being an American... listening to the stupid shit we have to deal with in this country."[11]

Today's autocrats seem to follow the model of Vladimir Putin's brand of faux democracy that is popular with the Russian people – foment confusion by creating chaos, blame others for your problems, control the media to instill devotion, demand an obedient populace and punish your enemies. Russian sociologist Yuri Lavada called it a new breed of human to replace economic man – "Homo Sovietus."[12] And these techniques are working.

> In Great Britain, the portion of people who favor "a strongman ruler who does not bother with elections" doubled from 25 percent a few decades ago to 50 percent.[13]

Many politicians find it convenient that complaining about the evils of government avoids the need to improve education, build infrastructure, support advanced research, provide welfare services and form international alliances. Richard Haas called it "The Great Abdication."[14]

Francis Fukuyama, who proclaimed the fall of communism as "The End of History," now admits he was wrong about the triumph of capitalism and democracy: "Twenty-five years ago, I didn't have a sense about how democracies can go backward. Now I think they clearly can."[15]

---

10   Max Fisher and Josh Keller, "What Explains US Mass Shootings?" (*New York Times*, Nov 7, 2017)

11   Michael Gerson, "The Madness of Conservatives" (*Washington Post*, May 26, 2017)

12   Carlos Lozada, "The Early Chapters" (*Washington Post*, Jun 15, 2018)

13   Yascha Moundk, "How Populist Uprisings Could Bring Down Liberal Democracy" (*Guardian*, Mar 4, 2018)

14   Richard Haas, "America and the Great Abdication" (*Atlantic*, Dec 2017)

15   Ishaan Tharoor, "The Man Who Declared 'The End of History' Fears for Democracy's Future" (*Washington Post*, Feb 9, 2017)

# The Trump Saga: A Case Study in the Power of Social Media

The amazing rise of Donald Trump to US president was a historic event that illustrates the political crisis gripping the globe. The Trump saga offers an important case study in how the power of social media can shape public consciousness and nourish the roots of autocracy. The following analysis explores this phenomenon at the symbolic, economic and political levels.

## Symbolic Level of Analysis: America's First Reality TV President

It can be clarifying to note the obvious – Donald Trump was not a traditional president. To a great extent, he was by his own admission actually playing the role of a "Reality TV President," constantly re-inventing as he went along. Trump regarded the presidency as a remarkable opportunity to act out a drama in which he starred. He told his aides to "think of each day as an episode in a TV show in which he vanquishes rivals."[16] Like Republican idol Ronald Reagan, Trump is also an actor, gifted at influencing the media to sway opinion.

The symbolic essence of Donald Trump can be seen in his use of "executive time," alone in his quarters at night. It is reported that President Trump would watch multiple TVs to check who was "winning" and firing off blistering tweets in response to opposition

This is a fascinating lesson in the art of shaping consciousness. With all his faults, Donald Trump is a genius at influencing public opinion, as shown when he came out of almost nowhere to win an "impossible" election. President Trump's challenge to reality has thrust the US into a post-factual world, igniting the Age of Consciousness and creating a lingering cloud of confusion.

---

16    Maggie Haberman et al., "Inside Trump's Hour-By-Hour Battle for Self-Preservation" (*New York Times*, Dec 9, 2017); James Poniewozik, "The Real Donald Trump is a TV Character" (*New York Times*, Sep 8, 2019)

## Economic Level of Analysis: Trumpism Could End Reaganomics

The US economy moves in long-term cycles, and President Trump's ascendancy could be the end of the conservative era that began with the election of Ronald Reagan in 1980. Since then, American thought has been dominated by a belief in the faults of government, the primary importance of free markets, and the imperatives of lower taxes and fewer regulations. While this ideal of "Reaganomics" boosted the economy, it also ballooned the Federal debt, led to crashing markets, and concentrated wealth to levels comparable to those preceding the Great Depression.

Global debt, considered dangerous at 100 percent of GDP, now exceeds 300 percent.[17]

Trumpism hearkened back to a time when coal, oil, and factory work dominated the economy, white males were supreme, and the rich consumed lavishly. To many, the Trump era seemed a last gasp attempt to revive a dying philosophy in the face of massive change. Historically, the decline of Trumpism may now bring the Era of Reaganomics to a close.

## Political Level: The Trump Failure Leaves a Political Vacuum

President Trump was elected because several crucial events coalesced to form an historic political upset; it was called a "failure of democracy." A vocal minority was angry over lost jobs, fearful of the growing power of women and ethnic minorities, hateful of government and ready to revolt. Russia's propaganda flooded the media with fake news. The FBI director announced more investigations into Hillary Clinton's emails two weeks before the election, at a crucial point when Trump was reeling from videos admitting he harassed women. And even though Clinton won the popular vote by more than the projected 2 percent, the Electoral College so favored rural and southern states that it swung the election to her opponent. A Gallup poll found that 75 percent of voters were "surprised" by the election of Donald Trump.[18]

---

17    Robert Samuelson, "The $ 217 Trillion Global Debt Bomb" (*Washington Post,* Jul 18, 2018)

18    "How People Describe Their Reactions to the Election" (*Gallup,* Nov 2016)

Trump's approval ratings were lower than any recorded for a president, and a strong majority of Americans considered his election a "mistake." Trump himself confirmed: "The election could have been held 20 times, but that was probably the one day I would have won. Everything came together at once."[19]

When the Trump Era ended with the pandemic and the resulting recession, support collapsed, even among Republicans. Staunch conservatives like Michael Gerson, George Will and David Brooks abandoned ship and urged people to vote Democratic. Columnist Kathleen Parker spoke for many conservatives when she lamented, "So, yes, the Grand Old Party is dead. Today, it's just the old party, peopled largely by a fading generation and powered by stale ideas."[20]

The climax in this saga was reached after Trump lost the 2020 election but promoted his "big lie" that "we won by a landslide, but the election was rigged." On January 6, 2020, history noted the first time an American president tried to stage a coupe d'état by urging his followers to storm the Halls of Congress.

The telling thing about this insurrection is that Trump was fascinated by watching his followers attack Congress. He was so glued to his TVs that he could not be convinced to call for help. Once again, this revealing incident reminds us that Donald Trump was still a reality TV actor playing the role of president.

What is the significance of this remarkable saga of the Trump Era? In retrospect, the "Trump rebellion" can be seen as a conservative counterpart to the "liberal rebellion" of the '60s; it even included the same riots and takeover of public buildings. The rise of Trumpism drives home the lesson that almost anybody with charisma can dominate the social media, and to gain unprecedented power.

In a time when it seems impossible to sort out lies from truth, how do we prevent mass delusion from distorting public policy? Regulation of social media may be able to control disinformation, though at some potential cost to freedom of speech. Beyond that, nobody knows, as consciousness is an untamed frontier. Chapter Eight will show that methods for mastering consciousness can help us become more self-aware and cultivate a responsible wisdom.

19 Joe Scarborough, "Gravity is Tugging at Trump" (*Washington Post*, Jul 27, 2018)

20 Parker, "How the GOP Can Be Reborn" (*Washington Post*, Feb 10, 2021); Jonathan Rauch and Benjamin Wittes, "Boycott the GOP" (*The Atlantic*, Mar 2018); George Will, "Trump Tweets, Mueller Indicts" (*National Catholic Reporter*, Dec 14, 2018)

However, those 74 million Trump supporters represent the problems facing democracy. Nations around the globe are reeling from public dissatisfaction with government bureaucracies that roll on unconcerned with their citizens' needs. Brexit is a prime example, as well the rise of autocrats noted above.

Neither the Republicans nor the Democrats can solve the enormous challenges ahead, leaving the country in a political vacuum. The Biden Administration offered the promise of working across the aisles, but the obstacles are enormous. President Biden would have to pacify Trump supporters, control the pandemic, tax the wealthy, improve health care, support people of color, rebuild infrastructure, address climate change, transform immigration and repair global relations – all while fending off charges of socialism. This seems unlikely, but his success in doing so could prove a tipping point in the decline of autocrats everywhere.

## Without Vision, the People Perish

The main question raised by all this turbulence is, how to fill the political vacuum? The conservative ideology of tax cuts and deregulation seems to have run its course, and liberals seem bent on advocating more government. What solutions are likely? Desirable?

Powerful forces of change are underway. The Millennial generation is demanding action on climate change, gun controls, immigration, cultural diversity and universal health care.[21] Women are gaining influence and power. Even Steve Bannon concurs: "The time has come. Women are gonna take charge of society."[22] And the "cultural creatives" who favor progressive values are growing to include roughly half of the nation.[23]

What is needed now is a vision that can guide this energy into political and government systems that work. As the Bible stated so well: "Where there is no vision, the people perish."[24]

I don't presume to define some ideal society; I leave that to others. What I can suggest is that Americans, and citizens of other nations, look for fresh applications

21    Dana Milbank, "It's the Kids Who Will Save Us" (*Washington Post,* Mar 25, 2018)

22    "Bannon to GOP: The Women Are Coming" (*BusinessWeek*, Feb 19, 2018)

23    See Sohail Inayutullah, "Trump: The Beginning or the End?" (*Journal of Future Studies*, Mar 2017); Richard Florida, *Rise of the Creative Class* (New York: Basic Books, 2012)

24    Proverbs 29:18, King James Version

of our heritage of democracy and free enterprise. These two foundational principles remain valid because they are based on the value of knowledge and intelligence – the collective knowledge of the governed through representative government, and the intelligent choices of individuals driving a market economy.

The problem is that these two ideals are so seldom practiced. Most corporations, governments and other organizations are hierarchical systems, albeit showing a warm face wherever they can. And political parties seem to have gravitated to opposing poles of the political spectrum. Republicans focus on the free enterprise end supporting business, while Democrats favor the democratic end advocating government solutions. I suggest the most strategic aspect of a viable vision would be to unite these two halves of the nation.

In the midst of polarization that has frozen nations into inaction, creative solutions are always available, but not in remedies of the past scarred by political battles between left and right. The opportunities lie in that no-man's land in the center, where politicians are fearful of taking fire from both sides – the radical middle.[25] The middle has been largely empty for decades because it is so forbidding. But it also offers unusual opportunities for political breakthroughs uniting left and right, and we badly need breakthroughs.

Leaders who can wade into the debate may find political gains by demonstrating what has been called the "politics of cooperation." Knowledge is still power in an Age of Consciousness, and collaborative problem-solving offers the advantage of increasing knowledge for all parties. This has been called the "loaves and fishes" theory – everybody wins.[26] Ideally, it is even conceivable that brave politicians could outcompete their opponents by showing they are better able to cooperate over the most polarizing issues that also offer the biggest gains.

Yes, I fully realize this seems a futile hope, as politicians are notorious for clinging to the fierce opposition that burdens their profession. The point of this chapter, and the entire book really, is that there is little hope for the future without transformative change. The previous chapter showed that corporations recognize the need to cooperate with stakeholders if we are to have a future at all. If business can change so dramatically, why not government and politics? It all depends on a shift in consciousness.

25    Mark Satin, *Radical Middle: The Politics We Need Now* (New York: Basic Books, 2004)

26    See the comments by Ray Smith, former CEO of Bell Atlantic, in my anthology, *The Infinite Resource: Creating and Leading the Knowledge Enterprise* (San Francisco: Jossey-Bass, 1998)

Following are a few examples of creative solutions from the center. It is in these directions that modern nations can embrace the global consciousness needed to resolve the MegaCrisis.

## A Carbon Tax Could Boost the Environment into a Major Industrial Sector

The Americans for Carbon Dividends offers what is thought to be "the most cost-effective, equitable and politically-viable climate solution." They propose taxing carbon and dropping command-and-control regulations that would then become obsolete. The income (about US$2000 per person per year) would be returned to taxpayers and invested in environmental research, alternative energy and green companies, boosting clean economic growth.[27]

After decades of stalemate, a solution could resolve the biggest crisis of our time by uniting the interests of conservatives, liberals, environmentalists, the public and corporations. This approach to controlling carbon emissions would disincentivize the use of fossil fuels by internalizing the social costs and allowing market forces to seek optimal solutions. The International Monetary Fund said carbon taxes are "the single most powerful tool" for solving the carbon problem.[28] California, the fifth-largest economy in the world, is pursuing these ideas with good success.[29]

The environment is actually a great opportunity in disguise. Green business investment worldwide is US$1.6 trillion, and revenues should reach several trillion dollars a year. It also produces more than 8 million jobs, more than in fossil fuels, and their numbers are growing faster.[30] Amory Lovins and Paul Hawken estimate that the environment produces US$33 trillion annually in social and economic benefits.[31] By viewing the environment as a foundation for a healthy planet and a healthier economy, this simple but powerful shift in consciousness could turn a global mess into sound economic growth and sustainable lifestyles.

---

27    John Schwartz, "New Group, With Conservative Credentials, Plans to Push for Carbon Tax" (*New York Times*, Jun 19, 2018)

28    "A Compelling Case For a Carbon Tax" (*Washington Post*, Oct 21, 2019)

29    See "EPA's War with California Proves America Needs a Carbon Tax" (*Guardian*, Dec 18, 2018)

30    "Jobs in Renewable Energy" (*eesi*, Feb 15, 2017)

31    Amory Lovins, Hunter Lovins, Paul Hawken, "A Road Map for Natural Capitalism" (*Harvard Business Review*, Jul-Aug 2007)

# The US Could Provide a Market Model of Universal Health Care

The US remains the only modern nation without some form of universal health care. The American laissez-faire approach costs roughly twice that of other nations, with mediocre results and about 31 million uninsured as of 2020. But we could greatly improve the Affordable Care Act's (ACA) system by making a few basic changes. The ACA is built on the basic features of a "managed market" that combine the power of competition and government controls.

Markets can only function well when buyers have sound information on price and value to guide their choices. Today, however, patients must make their decisions in an information vacuum, forced to rely on neighbors to recommend a heart surgeon, for instance. A good health-care system would be intelligent enough to help people choose among available health plans and find those best suited for their needs at minimal cost. It would gather sound outcome data and compare the medical performance of providers. Governments would provide subsidies and penalties, ensuring standards and other controls agreed upon politically. It could include a public option, while states, corporations, and other groups could always choose other plans. Universal participation could be achieved by simply enrolling anyone visiting a health-care provider.

American culture is committed to markets, and this could create a well-performing government market to provide universal health care, possibly at lower cost and with better service. That would be a great example to the world of combining free enterprise and good government.

## Accountability and Choice Can Make Government Lean and Dynamic

The idea of managed markets can provide the same dynamic benefits throughout government. This combination of accountability and freedom of choice is the key to creating lean and dynamic organizations. That's why business is keen on developing agile systems.

A good example comes from Mexico City. Customers suffered delay and indifference applying for licenses from a large bureaucracy. The same employees were dispersed into small competing neighborhood units in which teams were paid in proportion to their unit's performance. Within weeks, service became prompt and courteous, speeding up the process from months to days.

Imagine a postal system in which the neighborhood post office is staffed by a self-selected team committed to making their unit thrive. Evaluations of client satisfaction, revenue, costs and other goals would rate performance, guide improvements and reward employees with attractive pay. General tasks, such as mail sorting and delivery would be treated as overhead, or possibly turned into self-managed enterprises in their own right. Be sure to allow wide freedom to innovate, support teams with training and advice, and improve the system to approach the ideal of perfect markets. Then watch the market work.

The same concept is sweeping through American education as charter schools and choice compete with public schools. In Washington, DC, half of all schools are now chartered, adding a concern for performance and choice throughout the city. Almost all government services could be improved dramatically by introducing market mechanisms to create a dynamic breed of "public enterprise." Mayor Steve Goldsmith transformed the city of Indianapolis, Indiana, into a less costly market-based system providing superior service. Goldsmith said, "We tried everything, but nothing changed until we introduced competition."[32]

During the Clinton presidency, Vice President Al Gore made a strong start at "reinventing government" along similar lines. But the program halted when the election went to George W. Bush. Bringing back these powerful ideas is long overdue.

## How to Manage the Threat of Mass Unemployment

The fear that advanced AI will eliminate almost all jobs is palpable as automation promises to replace much human employment in the practice of law, medicine, teaching, and all professions. Half of all jobs may disappear, but there is always a new frontier of work. We simply do not understand yet how human abilities can replace the jobs now being lost.

32   *The Infinite Resource*, Op. Cit.

Studies noted in the previous chapter show this new frontier lies beyond knowledge in the complex arenas of creativity, judgment, and collaboration practiced by entrepreneurs, managers, artists and other roles that machines can't perform.[33] Structural unemployment is inevitable, but with some help it could be temporary while transitioning to these more challenging jobs.

With such benefits, we should welcome automation. Sweden is known for embracing change, so it is not surprising that 80 percent of Swedes favor AI, whereas 70 percent of Americans are fearful.[34] Some examples find that a combination of humans guiding intelligent machines works best.

Governments could contain this threat by encouraging education in these fields of the future, helping communities develop their economies to attract new industries, supporting the unemployed while making career changes, and investing in R&D to grow business opportunities. With a little imagination and vision, the bulk of the labor force could enjoy more interesting, better-paid jobs in a high-tech world.

It would help to pay citizens a Guaranteed Minimum Income, or Universal Basic Income. Combining all welfare programs (unemployment benefits, food stamps, housing and medical assistance and the like) into a single payment would slash through much government bureaucracy, reducing the net cost to not much more than we spend now, providing a much-needed safety net to elevate the citizenry.

## Publicly Funded and Collaborative Elections Could Restore Democracy

American elections have become drawn out, combative, and overhyped marathons. While the British accomplish their elections in about one month, the US takes over two years, politicians must raise several billion dollars for campaigns, and debates have become a blood sport where almost anything goes. Americans are often aghast to end up with mediocre candidates. But why would reasonable people volunteer to undergo an ordeal that appeals mainly to egomaniacs?

---

33    Halal at al., "AI and Future Jobs" (*Journal of Future Studies*, Dec 2016)

34    Tim Folger, "Will We Continue to Get Smarter?" (*Scientific American*, Aug 22, 2012); See chess master Gary Kasparov's book, *Deep Thinking: Where Machine Intelligence Ends and Human Creativity Begins* (New York: Public Affairs/Perseus Books, 2017); Peter Goodman, "The Robots Are Coming, and Sweden is Fine" (*New York Times*, Dec 27, 2017)

It is a great irony that those who insist the government is incompetent are often the very people electing zealots who will not compromise to get things done. The endless fights over abortion, immigration, guns, infrastructure, etc., can actually be resolved with many good solutions, but approaches to them that might be effective are seldom considered out of sheer obstinacy. I hold the faint hope that more female politicians might break this spell to foster collaboration.

The central obstacle is the corrupting role of money. US politicians have become entrepreneurs selling their time and influence. Roughly half of their day is devoted to working in boiler rooms asking people to donate campaign funds. The armies of lobbyists, big contributors, PACs, and myriad special interests are legion. With more women and younger people in politics, it is conceivable that Americans could find the courage to enact some form of public campaign financing. This single act could allow politicians to return to their job of governing, and it would also relieve politics from the corrupting influence of money.

## Extend Democracy and Enterprise Throughout the System

These are simply a few examples of what can be done to fill the current political vacuum, but they suggest that striking changes are possible. Green taxes could solve the environmental crisis while also promoting healthy economic growth. A well-managed market could provide a uniquely American solution to health care. The same approach could also extend throughout government to transform bureaucracies into dynamic organizations that better serve the public at less cost. The threat of unemployment due to automation could be held in check with strategic support. And publicly funded, centrist elections could rejuvenate democracy.

The principles of democracy and free enterprise form two themes running through these solutions. Green taxes, managed markets, public enterprise, accountability, choice, competition are various aspects of free enterprise applied to ease the burden of bureaucracy. And collaboration, public service, social responsibility, teamwork and transparency describe democratic practices that are sorely needed.

The current threat of autocratic regimes may take years to resolve, and some nations will always prefer a strong hand. The solution lies in looking to the faults of our cumbersome democracies and unstable economies. Any vision worth its salt must apply the genius of democracy and free enterprise throughout the nation, from the national level down to the grassroots, if we hope to survive the complexity of a high-tech world. These are demanding changes that require bold, heroic leadership, and they are risky. Some will fail. But a move to collaborative politics can offer prospects for better government.

# CHAPTER SIX

# Virtual Education and Higher-Order Skills: The Uneasy Shift from Teaching to Learning

Education is basically a transfer of knowledge, so it's not surprising that this book's theme, *Beyond Knowledge,* would raise difficult issues about teaching and learning.

Billions of people around the world are taking continuing-education courses via distance learning. Various online platforms are gaining wide usage, including virtual tutors, Massive Open Online Courses (MOOCs), TED talks, YouTube and the Kahn Academy lectures. Bill Gates said recently, "Soon, you'll find the best lectures in the world on the web for free."

These trends promise to raise a flood of tough questions:

- Considering the upheavals wrought by the PC and the smartphone in just the past decade, how much disruptive change will schools have to prepare for in the coming decades? Change will be exponential.

- With virtual education (VE) everywhere, how will teachers and schools cope with the changing needs of their market? They will shift to coaching.

- What will a young student need to learn over the roughly 100 years of projected life expectancy? A child born today must learn to surmount unprecedented changes in a few decades when a Space Age should be in full swing.

- As AI moves into schools and colleges, will automated instruction replace the traditional in class approach to teaching? Both approaches will co-exist.

- Will teachers suffer mass unemployment? No, their jobs will become more challenging.

- Will educational markets and organizations change? Yes, in a big way.

These are some of the challenges that education is facing increasingly today. This chapter examines the transformation underway as VE enters widespread use. I draw on many years of university teaching to explore the impacts of new educational technologies, student-centered learning, future career opportunities, university structures and the use of visualization methods. The conclusion is that schools are challenged to move *beyond knowledge and teaching.* Now they must embrace the need to assist active learners in finding their own understanding, creativity and purpose. Once again, this requires a major shift in consciousness

# Technology Extending Classroom Instruction

Access to high-quality VE is increasing as more intelligent teaching systems using AI and augmented/virtual reality enter the educational market. With rising college costs and graduates left with staggering student loans, online education is gaining in popularity, while expensive college degrees are losing favor. Georgia Tech offers an online MS in computer science for less than $7,000.[1]

> Oculus offers education programs in Taiwan, Japan and Seattle that give virtual reality (VR) headsets to libraries, museums and schools to promote understanding of how VR can aid learning and collaboration.[2]

VE provides results that are comparable to classroom instruction, yet in a way that is far more convenient and cost-effective, especially for teaching languages, math, statistics and other well-established fields.[3] Elite colleges entered the field when Stanford's first MOOCs started a movement to automate university courses. Many online students are busy working, mainly full-time employees, military personnel, housewives and the disabled. These working people use VE courses to enter new occupations as technology makes old ones obsolete. And VE is serving poor regions where high-quality education is rare. An MIT student was admitted after he earned a perfect score on a free electronics course while working online from his home in Mongolia.

High schools are moving fast to adopt virtual teaching, and colleges are almost there. Even elementary schools are going online as teachers use computer systems to deliver video lessons and assignments to students. Children in Japan are being given tablets designed to help them visualize science experiments.[4]

Box 6 summarizes examples of creative VE being developed at the leading edge of innovation.

1   Melissa Korn, "Online Degree Hits Learning Curve" (*Wall Street Journal*, Dec 13, 2015)

2   "Announcing Oculus Education Pilot Programs in Taiwan, Japan and Seattle" (*Oculus VR*, Aug 28, 2018)

3   Dhirendra Kumar, "Pros and Cons of Online Education" (*North Carolina State University*, Aug 19, 2015)

4   "Japanese Schools Plan to Replace Textbooks with Tablets" (*South China Morning Post*, Jun 30, 2016)

## Box 6: Exemplars of the Leading Edge of Education

**Elite Colleges Organize Global Education** The Massachusetts Institute of Technology (MIT) leads the Open Courseware Consortium, which organizes universities around the world to use free online courses. Stanford offers online courses through edX, Coursera, and Udacity. Worldwide, about 250 institutions offer open courses.

**The MOOC Revolution** Coursera's MOOCs have grown to include more than 115 universities and over 22 million students. The service is expanding from engineering, math, and computer science into medicine, poetry, and history. The American Council on Education is giving college credits to online courses.

**Virtual Tutoring** Gooru, Knewton, and Affectiva use virtual tutoring for individualized lessons that adapt to student's strengths and weaknesses, teach through games, and track a student's engagement. This global market reached US$103 billion, a small fraction of the $1.48 trillion education market.

**Corporate Training** Coursera, Udacity, and many other popular platforms have designed programs exclusively for corporate training.

**Military Games** The US. Defense Department is developing games such as MiLands (Military Lands), a virtual world in Second Life, to train fighters from all services. Pew Research projects that this practice, known as gamification, will be in everyday use for education and training.

**The Cornucopia of Internet Courses** The TED organization offers customizable lessons. The Khan Academy offers more than 10,000 video tutorials to over 48.5 million registered users. YouTube EDU has 600 partners, including the Smithsonian Institution, who are providing educational videos for direct access by schools. Udemy has 24 million students choosing from 80,000 courses.

Despite its strengths, online education has yet to overcome serious problems. More than half of students complete smaller online courses, but under five percent complete courses with large enrollments. Only one-fourth of teens in households with yearly incomes less than US$35,000 have laptops, compared with 62 percent in those with US$100,000 or more per year.[5]

Many colleges have found that VE courses are not sustainable financially because they are more expensive to produce, requiring special software, faculty training, instructional designers and student support. The University of California, Berkeley, dropped its online platforms because they proved too costly. Kaplan, a supplier of

---

5    Natasha Singer, "The Digital Disparities Facing Lower-Income Teenagers" (*New York Times*, Nov 3, 2015)

higher education and test-preparation courses, sold its online high school business after it proved unsuccessful.[6]

These are simply the usual growing pains, however, and VE is expected to expand rapidly as the programs becomes more sophisticated. While the teacher-led classroom remains the standard, the 2020 coronavirus pandemic forced schools to adopt VE, and it may now continue to be used to a large extent. TechCast experts think online learning is likely to reach 30-percent adoption levels about 2025. Market saturation is estimated to reach global demand of about US$700 billion/year at about 2040.

## The Convergence of VE and Traditional Teaching

The big question on most minds is, will VE disrupt the traditional classroom, much as Uber disrupted the taxi industry? With the cost of a college degree, including lost pay, running almost a half-million dollars, why would people not choose an online program instead? In the UK, students often are left owing as much 30,000 to 60,000 pounds upon graduation, and the same happens in the US.[7] That is why the University of Phoenix and other online colleges are expanding, and more are certain to come.

Yet people continue to seek degrees in person – why? The traditional four-year college experience is so deeply ingrained in modern life that it is almost sacrosanct, a critical rite of passage and an essential way to acquire social skills, contacts and worldview. But "old" media like movies still thrive after being disrupted by TV and video, and books remain popular despite all manner of online reading. In much the same way, in-class education is likely to enjoy continued demand for the foreseeable future. Both VE and class instruction are expected to serve different markets as the need for education expands into one of the great industries of our time.

Some teachers and schools resist the use of computer learning because they want students to think, rather than using technology as a supplemental tool.[8] It is hard to convey complex ideas online, and VE slights the personal interaction needed to develop the social skills provided by good teachers. This means that VE is a strong tool

6    Carl Straumsheim, "Online Education Costs More, Not Less" (*Inside Higher Ed*, Feb 17, 2017)

7    Rohit Talwar et al., "Education and Employment and Response to Automation" (*University World News*, Jul 20, 2018)

8    Cathie Norris and Elliot Soloway, "Why Has Technology Failed to Substantially Improve Student Achievement?" (*The Journal*, Mar 4, 2015)

for traditional education, but teacher-led classrooms still have an edge for developing higher-order skills, as we will see soon.

What is likely to change is the convergence of these two streams of instruction. Those teaching VE increasingly realize that a few face-to-face meetings are needed to establish that essential rapport between teacher and student, while classroom teaching is enriched by various online methods. Blending these education models has the potential to leverage the knowledge-building power of VE into classrooms, homes, offices and anywhere, actually.

## The Virtual University

Now let's examine the impacts that are likely to roll through higher education. Anybody living almost anywhere in the world should soon be able to find any course that interests them, probably for free. The opportunities to learn are endless with the MIT consortium involving 250 universities, MOOCs being offered to 22 million students, and TED, YouTube and the Khan Academy providing almost limitless instruction online. Kahn alone offers 10,000 video tutorials to almost 50 million users.

All these forms of education are now converging to create the "virtual university." Whether a traditional classroom setting or VE, a stunning variety of online resources should enrich the learning process. Virtual lectures by famous people are increasingly being piped into classrooms via video conferencing. With intelligent tutorials and MOOCs becoming available on almost any topic, it is hard to justify the normal lecture time spent in classrooms. Instead, students can do more challenging work on research projects, consulting, community service, field studies, group work and endless other possibilities.

Wired campuses now allow students and faculty to interact from anywhere at any time. Carnegie Mellon University has connected its campus with the Open Learning Initiative, which uses computerized tutors to teach routine subjects and has students work in virtual teams on real-world problems that cut across disciplines. Each year, around 50,000 students participate in their online academic courses.

In addition to coursework, "knowledge on-demand" is likely to be available to help repair a gadget, solve a problem or even perform a surgical operation. A "killer tutorial app," possibly using Augmented Reality (AR), may enter widespread use to convey knowledge cheaply and conveniently. And with AI improving language translation, this global knowledge base could be accessed by people speaking different languages around a world badly in need of understanding.

The net effect is to subtly but effectively transform the classroom from a physical place to an information network that can be accessed almost everywhere in the virtual university.

## From Bureaucracy to Self-Managed Faculty

This movement towards a virtual university will require serious rethinking of academic institutions. Having taught at several universities, I am sorry to say most are managed badly by today's standards. Although corporations, governments and most other organizations have struggled to become accountable and flexible, higher education has remained largely aloof from these forces of change. My colleagues and I joke about how universities are relics of a past dominated by large, top-down bureaucracies, the last bastion of socialism.

For instance, it is hard to find a meaningful relationship between the performance of teaching units and their budgets. Resources are allocated to different schools according to some mysterious rules inherited from the past, leaving those getting more with little incentive to improve, while those getting less feel disgruntled and also without incentive.

Instead of rewarding performance, control is exercised by bureaucratic systems. It's not surprising that most faculty show little interest in increasing their student load and actively strive to avoid teaching. This bureaucracy is primarily responsible for the notorious cost increase of college education, which is roughly double that of inflation in the US.

It is especially ironic that business schools like mine, supposedly a source of innovation, are among the most bureaucratic. We have tons of professors who have never had a real job, much less run a business. Yet, they are supposed to teach managers something useful. This same divide between theory and practice can be seen in the resistance to real-world projects. When I founded TechCast as a new venture out of my Emerging Technologies course, my colleagues were shocked; some even saw it as a conflict of interest to start a business – in a business school!

Of course, many schools and colleges are well managed and innovative, as attested by the exemplars at the leading edge mentioned above. If universities are to compete in the complex arena of VE, however, serious structural changes are required to encourage entrepreneurship and innovation. As heretical as it may seem to academic sensitivities, the main need is to redefine teaching departments as the equivalent of profit-centers, as also recommended by McKinsey, a major consulting firm.[9]

Ideally, departments should be held accountable for class sizes, quality research, student satisfaction, publications and other academic goals, in addition to revenue generated. Faculty could then be encouraged to work as self-managed teams rewarded for performance with freedom to innovate. Academia is one of our most conservative institutions, so the prospects for such changes appear to be slim. But business and other innovative institutions are moving into education, and competition is a powerful force.

## Careers of the Future

Finally, technological and institutional changes in education will be meaningful only if they can provide the skills necessary to survive a rapidly changing, more difficult world. We saw in a previous chapter that the automation of routine work is likely to bring forth a new class of creative tasks performed by entrepreneurs, leaders, consultants, coordinators and endless other jobs requiring that human touch. Something similar is happening in education.

These demanding skills are increasingly being provided with a variety of more practical approaches. Short intensive programs immerse students in special training quickly and conveniently. Graduate education is growing to provide training in specialized fields; it is estimated that 80 percent of new jobs will require advanced degrees. Corporations and governments are developing educational programs for

---

9    Bernard T. Ferrari and Phillip H. Penn, "Universities and the Conglomerate Challenge" (*McKinsey Quarterly,* Sep 2018)

their organization's needs, paying employees to study, providing college funding and canceling student debt.

In addition, the tech revolution suggests that exotic new careers are likely. We can anticipate exciting opportunities for Robo-Nannies, End of Life Planners, Human Enhancement Technicians, Robot Whisperers, Autonomous Vehicle Ethicists and who knows what else?[10] Education is being challenged to keep up.

> The University of Michigan's School of Business launched a program that allows students to attend classes throughout their careers.[11]

One can imagine college campuses competing with a flood of innovative online courses and degrees, many driven by business forces. Bold programs could forfeit degrees altogether to focus on cutting-edge work needed by high-tech companies. Some companies now train their own employees rather than hire college graduates. Singularity University in Silicon Valley is so attractive at educating people on cutting edge technologies that highly qualified students flock to attend, although no degrees are offered

Google's "Professional Career Certificate" program takes applicants with no prior college and provides the equivalent of a four-year degree at a cost of US$300 in three to six months. Working on data analysis, project management and other professional fields, graduates can expect to earn an average of US$93,000 in time. Microsoft offers a similar program, and it is expected that the trend will spread to other industries.[12]

The motivating forces behind these company-sponsored apprenticeships are growing with the advance of a high-tech work environment. Change is so rapid that traditional colleges can't keep pace with employers' needs for a highly skilled workforce. And employees are hard-pressed to devote four years and tens of thousands of dollars for a college education that may be obsolete upon graduation.

---

10     For more possibilities, see Rohit Talwar et al., "What Will Our Children Do? 20 Jobs of the Future" (*Training*, Aug 31, 2018)

11     Danielle Paquette, "In the Future, College Never Ends" (*Washington Post*, Jun 6, 2018)

12     "Will You Still Need a College Education in 2240?" (*Fast Company*, Jan 29, 2020); David Leibowitz, "You Don't Need College Anymore" (*Medium*, Aug 5, 2020)

> As the cost of college continues to rise faster than inflation, Google, Microsoft, Apple, Ernst & Young and other powerful companies no longer require employees to have degrees.[13]

Partially as a response to this competition, education seems to be in the early stages of shifting away from the "butts in seats" approach and toward "competency-based," or "proficiency-based," learning. Rather than having teachers bear the responsibility for actual learning that takes place, this innovative concept puts the responsibility where it belongs – on the student.

With the support of their teachers, students are then asked to use whatever resources they prefer – the teacher's instruction, Internet, VE or other sources – and then demonstrate the required skills and knowledge needed to earn course grades and degrees. It's the ultimate in student-led learning. One high school student said, "Classes here are more self-led. Your teachers are not talking at you. It's more of an open conversation." And a teacher concurred, "It's really getting back to why we became teachers: the students."[14]

## Teaching and Learning Beyond Knowledge

What can we learn by integrating these trends into a meaningful whole? A vibrant global marketplace and abundant free enterprise should drive a rich diversity of products and services to transform education continuously. Just as Moore's Law doubles computer progress every two years, educational technologies will also improve vastly every few years.

For instance, a really good ground-breaking AI tutor that students love for its charming effectiveness could prove as popular as your favorite GPS navigation voice or the Alexa in your kitchen. The biggest change could be the use of video, sophisticated games, simulations, AR and VR applications, crowdsourcing experiments, and even holographic images to engage people realistically.

---

13    Megan Mcardle, "Imagine a World Without Mandatory College Degrees" (*Washington Post*, Sep 1, 2018)

14    Tara Garcia, "Competency-Based Learning Takes Root" (*Washington Post*, Jan 13, 2020)

The main shift should be the move to foster subjective higher-order skills. Like all aspects of the tech revolution, the automation of routine tasks drives a move beyond knowledge to the higher ground of consciousness. With all manner of tools available to help with memorization and learning, the real work of education should embrace those complex skills that machines can't provide – active learning, understanding, communication, creative problem-solving, leadership, action. Author Faisal Hoque says, "As we hurtle toward our inevitable robot-and-AI filled future, these uniquely human capabilities will only become more essential."[15]

Coursera co-founder Andrew Ng said, "One thing that Coursera doesn't do well is teach non-cognitive skills ... and 80 percent of your income are due to non-cognitive skills: teamwork, ethics, anxiety."[16]

A striking example of what lies ahead may be alternatives to standard test systems like the SAT, ACT, and AP. Rather than focus on the student's command of knowledge in critical subjects, a new venture called Imbellus uses dynamic video *gaming systems* to place candidates in a simulated natural environment that tests their ability to think, reason, make decisions and react quickly. Using AI, psychometrics, 3D animation and other advanced tools, Imbellus has proven more effective in developing the ability to perform in high-tech jobs. One student described the experience as "I became totally immersed. I forgot the world around me."[17]

Imbellus has proven more accurate than standard tests in determining a student's potential for academic studies and job performance, and the system eliminates the possibility of cheating. The world's top consulting firm, McKinsey, has used it to evaluate 5,000 job applicants in 20 countries and plans to double the number of candidates using the system. Imbellus even proposes transforming entire curricula to this new paradigm based on educating students to think and act in project-like situations more closely resembling real work in real jobs. Not surprisingly, the resistance is fierce from professors who like the old "sage on the stage" approach to teaching.

15   *Fast Company,* Op. Cit.

16   Emma Green, "What MOOCs Can't Teach" (*Atlantic*, Dec 16, 2013)

17   "The Way Out of College Admissions Hell is ... Video Games?" (*BusinessWeek*, Mar 20, 2019)

Beyond even creative work, there seems to be an emerging need to help students manage the challenges of personal identity, purpose and meaning that have formerly been relegated to clergy and therapists. The stress and confusion of a changing world are so great that students often are unable to cope. The American College Health Association reports that 52 percent of students feel hopeless, and 39 percent suffer from severe depression. Suicide rates among the young are unprecedented. That explains why Professor Laurie Santos at Yale has 1200 students enrolled in her course on "How to be happy."[18]

For all the reasons noted in this chapter, education is going to require dramatic changes to meet the needs of a world moving beyond knowledge. Today's teaching methods and organizations will prove a poor match for an expected 10 billion people from diverse cultures, the technology revolution, climate change and other global crises. The head of MIT's online program called VE "the biggest change since the printing press." As we like to say in academia, it should be a fascinating learning experience.

---

18   "How to be Happy," (*The Week*, Aug 17-24, 2018)

# CHAPTER SEVEN

# From Religion to Spirit: The Ultimate Technology of Consciousness

Controversy over religion is so rife that an attempt by the John Templeton Foundation to reconcile opposing views among scientists became a "free-for-all."[1] Nobel laureate Steven Weinberg said, "The world needs to wake up from its long nightmare of religious belief," and biologist Richard Dawkins claimed religion is "brainwashing" and "child abuse." While anthropologist Melvin Konner called Dawkins "simplistic and uninformed," and biologist Francisco Ayala cautioned, "To think we are going to persuade [all people in the world] to live a rational life based on scientific knowledge ... is like believing in the fairy godmother."

The divide between science and religion is eternal, but attitudes are changing. As we will see, authoritative surveys show that people are leaving organized religion – but at the same time, they are also drawn to believe in some form of "higher power." This critical trend highlights a move from the dogma of religion toward a growing hunger for the substance of spirituality. And the human spirit we defined in Chapter Three is driving this change.

Over the next few decades, roughly 10 billion educated people will pursue their spiritual interests in a world teeming with diverse cultures. As we have seen, the prevailing jumble of antiquated beliefs cannot get us through the MegaCrisis. Here's what is needed.

It is becoming apparent that some type of overarching belief system is needed to bring order to the gratuitous conflict, the self-interest and the outmoded logic of the past. Organized religion is dogmatic and out of touch, and the scientific view posits a cold, lifeless universe, devoid of human meaning. I will suggest that signs point to a third path.

Following our explorations of transformations in government, business, and education, we will explore how human spirit is likely to transform organized religion into a personal spirituality. In time, the rise of spirituality should form a global consciousness, ethics, or moral code, for a unified world. And since belief in higher powers, the purpose of life, the soul and other spiritual matters are so far reaching, spirituality should become the most powerful technology of consciousness (ToC), leading to a Mental/Spiritual Revolution.

---

1    George Johnson, "A Free-for-All on Science and Religion" (*New York Times*, Nov 23, 2006)

# The Genetic Roots of Religious Belief

It is almost impossible to understand religion without first understanding why it is universal. Every society professes some type of belief system (even communism, capitalism, and atheism) because a common belief system is *functional*. The world is abuzz with infinite information, and each individual must select those bits of knowledge that are essential for survival. While it is fairly easy in a small group to learn what others expect, a large community must rely on abstract beliefs to govern behavior. That's why rulers – from the ancient Mayans to the old politburo in the USSR to former President Trump in America – have carefully cultivated their followers' beliefs, with varying degrees of success. Belief systems set personal goals, ostracize unwanted behavior, ensure cohesiveness and otherwise meld individuals into a functional community.

Religions of various types have evolved to serve this basic need by channeling the universal quest for understanding the big questions (Why am I here? What is the purpose of life?) into elegant beliefs. Walking through the Museum of the American Indian in Washington DC, I was struck by the remarkably diverse belief systems invented by every tribe, without exception. Throughout history, untold numbers of religions have been invented, flourished for a while and disappeared in this evolutionary process, much like species of plants and animals.[2] The great religions that have endured are the survivors of this struggle amongst the most fit.

An important clue can be seen in the Life Cycle of Evolution (LCE) in Chapter One. It is telling that the "take-off point" coincides with the birth of the world's great surviving religions. Judaism, Christianity, Islam, and Buddhism all emerged between 500 BC to 600 AD, starting the rapid rise of civilization. This striking fact suggests that some type of religion seems essential to the advance of societies everywhere.

The foundational nature of spirituality can be seen in the Gobekli Tepe ruins in Turkey, the oldest known human structure. Researchers have found no practical purpose for the temple and have concluded that it was primarily a ceremonial center for the observance of religion. The ruins are estimated to be 11,600 years old, predating Stonehenge and the great pyramids, and even older than the agricultural

---

2    Ara Norenzayan, "The God Issue: Religion is the Key to Civilization" (*New Scientist,* Mar 19, 2012)

revolution. Anthropologists think this finding indicates that the invention of religion was necessary for the very start of civilization.[3]

Religions and ideologies unite a community and organize the maze of information flooding the brain into a workable framework, giving life purpose, guidance and meaning. Charles Darwin discovered evolution, but he also observed "A belief in spiritual agencies seems to be universal."

> Professor Huston Smith, the informal dean of religious studies, concluded "If we take the world's enduring religions at their best, we discover the distilled wisdom of the human race."[4]

Just as physical traits have emerged through the process of natural selection, so has the tendency for humans to have spiritual experiences. In Chapter Three, we noted that scientists attribute religious behavior to the evolution of genetic imprinting in our very brains. Much like the nature versus nurture issue, it is estimated that 40 to 50 percent of religious traits are genetically fixed and the remainder by cultural norms and individual choice.[5]

With such deep genetic roots, it should not be surprising to see that modern people today continue to hold beliefs in the supernatural, although they are becoming "spiritual but not religious." The variety of data can be confusing, but a few trends stand out. The percentage of Americans professing "no religion" increased from 8 percent in 1990 to 26 percent in 2019. But those who claim, "I don't believe in a personal God, but I do believe in a higher power of some kind" increased from 7 percent to 21 percent. Overall, 90 percent believe in God or a higher power. Even in Europe, where churches lie empty, 65 percent of the population believe in God or a higher power.[6]

Other trends suggest belief systems are so effective in promoting productive lives that "believers" are likely to dominate modern societies. This may be surprising,

---

3    Charles Mann, "The Birth of Religion" (*National Geographic*, Jun 2011)

4    Smith, *The World's Religions* (New York: Harper Collins, 2009)

5    David Warmflash, "Not in Our Stars but in Our DNA" (*Genetic Literacy Project*, Dec 17, 2012)

6    Neha Sahgal, "10 Key Findings About Religion in Western Europe" (PEW Research Center, May 29, 2018); "Fewer Americans Affiliate with Organized Religions, Belief and Practice Unchanged: Key Findings from the 2014 General Social Survey" (NORC, March 2015); Harriet Sherwood, "Why Faith is Becoming More Popular" (*The Guardian,* Aug 27, 2018)

but studies noted here and in Chapter Three contend that religious and spiritual people have better health, greater achievements and more children. One may not like the polarizing effects of religiosity, and more fertility is of doubtful value in an overcrowded world. Still, the fact is that the spiritually inclined are growing about twice the rate of non-believers, and this tendency is likely to spread widely. The Amish, for instance, have grown from 123,000 in 1991 to 249,000 in 2010 and seem headed for a total of 7 million in 2100. Something similar is underway in the developing world where roughly 90 percent of people are religious.[7]

## Spirituality Is Replacing Religion

The upshot is that the crisis in Christianity is leading to a severe loss of religious faith and a rise in spirituality instead. About 75 percent of young people in the US now say they are "spiritual but not religious."[8] And their elders, the baby boom generation, are entering maturity and they are looking for meaning in their passing lives.

I was raised a Catholic. I cherish wonderful memories of serving as an altar boy, and I continue to find a loving grace in the sacrament of mass. But the scandals of child abuse rocking the Catholic Church have taken a profound toll on the faithful, especially in the face of the hierarchy's failure to address the problem. This has not been helped by the Church's resistance to admitting women into the priesthood and its insistence on celibacy. And with a severe shortage of young priests entering seminaries, I find it hard to understand Rome's intransigence, especially as other faiths have accepted such changes rather well. In fact, the presence of women and married priests is exactly what seems needed at this crucial time for all these reasons.

The Catholic Church may recover in time, but these problems signify a far greater crisis – the passing of faith in religion. In an age where knowledge is widespread, why would people believe literally in these venerable but badly dated creeds? Many of my fellow Catholics disagree with the Church's teachings on abortion, gay rights, contraception, women in the priesthood and married priests. Yet they seek something more spiritually nourishing than science. Modern science has shown us the awesome

7    "Religion May Have Evolved Because of its Ability to Help People Exercise Self-Control" (*Physorg*, Dec 30, 2008); "Model Predicts 'Religiosity Gene' Will Dominate Society" (*Physorg*, Jan 28, 2011)

8    Philip Clayton, "Letting Doubters in the Door" (*Los Angeles Times*, Mar 26, 2012)

beauty of an infinite universe, but this does not provide moral guidance. Spirituality is starting to fill that gap.

> David Tracey, an Australian professor and author of *The Spirituality Revolution*, expressed the challenge well: "We are caught in a difficult moment in history, stuck between a secular system we have outgrown and a religious system we cannot fully embrace."[9]

If spirituality is becoming more influential, we should pause to define this nebulous concept. What makes spirituality different from religion, and how is it better? One approach would be to compare it to the difference between teaching and learning described in Chapter Six. Just as schools are challenged to focus on the student instead of the curriculum, spirituality challenges us to move from the institution of religion to the individual seeking salvation. Religion relies on authority to enforce beliefs; spirituality draws on available wisdom to ease suffering and find our way on life's journey.[10] Religion is the institution, while spirit is the substance.

In most churches, I am left wanting by the abstract, theoretical language used by priests, the way theology is expressed in terms of divine figures to be adored and worshiped, the lack of guidance and examples of ordinary life lived well. In contrast, each time I walk into my garden, the sacred is immediately there. There is no theology. Nothing is abstract. The transcendent is alive before my eyes, and I walk in harmony with the powers that create and sustain life. This type of spiritual experience is direct and available to us everywhere, not only in a church, synagogue, mosque or temple. I may not understand the theology, but this is the living spirit I describe in many places throughout this book; the human spirit that is energized by nature, science, people, and a love for the transcendent.

This universal type of spirituality can be found in all religions, and that is why people today are increasingly ecumenical. They want to draw on the heritage of various faiths to seek the sacred. It is common today to find Christians who adhere to multiple faiths, who practice yoga, Zen meditation or tai chi or attend an Islamic service. True spirituality also finds no conflict with science but instead is ennobled

---

9    Tracey, *The Spiritual Revolution* (Sydney, Australia: Routledge, 2007)

10    See Gionanni Dienstmann, "Spirituality vs. Religion: The Future of Truth and Meaning" (*Live and Dare, Oct 12, 2018*)

by modern science's understanding of the universe, while science itself is enriched by understanding spiritual experience.

This universal presence of spirit can at times stun us with its unexpected power. Gallup polls find that 70 to 90 percent of Americans have had paranormal or peak experiences – feeling the presence of a deceased loved one, spiritual ecstasy, bodily healing, forebodings of a coming disaster, and so on. A survey of physicians found that 55 percent have witnessed "medical miracles."[11]

I can share an example of my own to help clarify. Like many people today, I have explored a variety of spiritual practices, with occasional breakthroughs. I volunteered once to help serve meals for homeless men. After a few weeks, I began to wonder why I was doing this. It was depressing to see those lost souls waiting in line with their shabby clothes looking tired and dispirited. To make matters worse, many of the other servers were sad people themselves, with their own problems of poverty, sexual identity and substance abuse. And the building was old and run down, adding to the gloom. I couldn't help but think, why am I here?

We servers usually gathered in a circle to pray before the meal was served. As we started to pray on a bleak day, I was particularly troubled by doubts, feeling torn and aching for guidance. Suddenly, out of nowhere, I was jolted by a flash of energy. It felt like a bolt of lightning, filling the air with warmth and love for my fellow servers, for the homeless men, for the entire world. Of my several spiritual experiences, this was most intense by far, leaving me quivering with ecstasy and enveloping us all in a circle of intensely bright light.

It was as if someone was saying – "This is why you are here."

## Global Ethics for a Unified World

If the previous trends hold true, this universal need for spirituality is likely to emerge as one of the great forces of our time. Earlier, I noted Teilhard de Chardin's belief that evolution would cover the planet in a web of consciousness. Today, the Digital

11   Sharon Begley, "Why We Believe" (*Newsweek*, Nov 3, 2008); David Moore, "Three in Four Americans Believe in Paranormal: Little change from similar results in 2001" (*Gallup News Service*, Jun 16, 2005); Kenneth Woodward, "They Need a Miracle" (*Newsweek*, Jan 31, 2005)

Revolution is realizing this vision by forming a rudimentary "global brain." A growing variety of technologies and billions of devices are uniting the world into a tangle of electronic connections. A board director of the New York Stock Exchange put it well: "We are going to reach a point where it's going to be one huge electronic market."[12] As Chapter One proclaimed, Teilhard's noosphere is here.

In the global equivalent of a brain, each person represents a neuron, forming trillions of synapse-like connections with billions of PCs, smartphones, video, television and endless other devices. Kevin Kelly, founder of *Wired* magazine, thinks the web is subsuming the knowledge of all humans into a "global central nervous system." He observed, "There is only one time in the history of each planet when its inhabitants first wire up its innumerable parts to make one large machine."[13] That time on Earth is now.

This digital integration of the globe is driving an equivalent need for collaboration, common values and a global code of ethics. Some type of global consciousness is almost unavoidable if the world hopes to meet the intersecting crises of climate change, sustainable energy, financial instability, machine intelligence, conflict and more problems to come. The mental and spiritual forces at the top of the Life Cycle of Evolution are especially powerful, and now the world faces the challenge of using them wisely.

> The Dalai Lama declared: "All major religious carry basically the same message of love, compassion, and forgiveness ... that should be part of our daily lives. But religion is no longer adequate. This is why I am convinced the time has come to find a way of thinking about spirituality and ethics beyond religion altogether."

The idea of a global consciousness follows logically, and some progress is emerging. Religions are largely based on common moral principles, corporations profess ethical codes, and most individuals believe in some set of universal values. As we will see below, a growing number of influential people advocate a global ethics that could unify people under a commonly accepted set of basic values and beliefs. Box 7 summarizes what is underway:

---

12    Thomas Heath, "NASDAQ CEO Is On a Mission" (*Washington Post,* Oct 14, 2018)

13    Kevin Kelly, *The Inevitable: Understanding the 12 Technological Forces That Will Shape Our Future* (New York: Viking, 2016)

# Box 7: Support for Global Ethics

**Vatican** Pope Benedict XVI declared that globalization requires a "common code of ethics" to combat poverty and ensure peace.

**United Nations** UN Deputy Secretary-General Jan Eliasson proclaimed a moral code for the 2030 Sustainable Development Agenda, adopted unanimously by 193 Heads of State.

**Internet and Social Media** Blogs and online publications are devoted to the message of harmony and peace. Examples include the Institute for Global Ethics and the School of Life, which is a global secular organization dedicated to developing emotional intelligence.

**International Association of Religious Freedom** The IARF is a century-old organization that meets annually to integrate religious thought and practice.

**World Council of Religious Leaders** This group of spiritual leaders in 2000 announced a "Commitment to Global Peace" intended to counter conflict, poverty and protect the environment.

**Religions for Peace** This is one of the first organizations to form a large alliance of religious leaders to fight poverty, save nature and prevent war.

**Universal Philosophy** Many philosophers and religious teachers (Baha'i, Mother Teresa, Osho Rajneesh) believe there is one universal God who is like a rainbow, with constituents of different religions forming different colors of the same spectrum.

TechCast's experts estimate that 30 percent of the world's people will adhere to a common set of ethical principles around 2030, with a very positive social impact. They think a global ethics would create the foundation for a functioning world system that contains conflict and promotes global order. Without a sense of worthy goals and purpose, no community can survive.

At the time of this writing in early 2021, the coronavirus pandemic and other threats like climate change are a stark reminder that the present global order is not sustainable. The reigning ideas inherited from the past are leading toward disaster. It is the passing of today's reigning ideology of capitalism, economic growth, money, power, self-interest and rationality. Prevailing practices in the US, as the most prominent example, have failed to address the climate crisis, inequality, universal health care, political gridlock and other parts of the MegaCrisis.

This global threat is so huge that it seems almost impossible to deal with. Without a shift in consciousness based on unity, cooperation and other essential beliefs, there seems little hope. But with a shift to global consciousness, it all becomes possible. The big question remaining is, "What should be the new vision, values, principles, and policies?" There have been many attempts to create such a moral code. TechCast has studied this problem, convened experts to resolve it, and tested the proposed solution in extensive workgroups across several organizations. We learned that the following five principles of global consciousness provide a simple framework that makes sense:

1. **Treat the Planet and All Life forms as Sacred** After trying for decades, the SETI Project — Search for Extraterrestrial Intelligence – has found no evidence of other civilizations. Many scientists are convinced other civilizations are out there, but they may be more distant or hard to detect. This rarity of life reminds us what a miracle planet Earth really is, and that we are responsible for its well-being.

2. **Govern the World as a Unified Whole** Nations remain the major players in the global order, but they should be coordinated by some type of global institution like the UN and other international bodies to encourage cooperation. Individuals should continue to be loyal to their nations and local institutions, but they should also accept their role as global citizens.

3. **Instill Democracy and Free Enterprise Throughout Institutions** The Business Roundtable announcement that all stakeholders should be treated equally with investors seems an historic breakthrough. This democratic form of enterprise could set a new standard for collaborative behavior and human values throughout modern societies.

4. **Embrace Diversity as an Asset** Rather than becoming a uniform pallid bureaucracy, a unified world should embrace the wondrous diversity of cultures and individuals. Working across differences is tough, but differences are also a source of knowledge, talents and human energy.

5. **Celebrate Community** Any society needs frequent opportunities to gather together in good spirit, enjoy differences and commonalities, and simply to celebrate life. With global communications common now, we could witness a flowering of celebratory events over the coming years to nourish the global soul.

An historic change in consciousness is hardly achieved overnight, and the obstacles posed by the status quo are formidable. But the rise of human spirit and the prospect of a Mental/Spiritual Revolution could change all that. This would be unprecedented, and we will see that it is likely in the next few years.

## The Coming Mental/Spiritual Revolution

If the move from religiosity to a global consciousness requires a Mental/Spiritual Revolution, how can we possibly believe this ambitious vision will be realized? Such a wrenching transformation would have to overcome enormous obstacles, even beyond the obvious threats of the Global MegaCrisis. Interest groups will resist the loss of privileges. Change will be hard, fast and constant, often driven by crisis. Confusion will reign, and leadership for this pivotal change must be found.

Drawing our analogy to the human life cycle again, we are reminded that the passage to global maturity would be roughly similar to the birth of a child or a teen's passage to adulthood, although on a global scale and with all the pain that implies. Much like the inevitability of a fetus leaving its mother's womb or a child maturing, evolution appears to be drawn naturally toward a metaphysical world that is beyond current understanding. This birth may abort in the face of the challenges noted above, but it is far more likely to succeed because it is normal in the life of a planet. If we could assess other countless civilizations that may exist throughout the universe, I suspect they would follow the same stages in the Life Cycle of Evolution.

This is hardly a random process. There are huge differences in scale, yet almost all children grow into successful adults. Similarly, the culmination of life on any planet probably is always drawn to a mature stage of consciousness. Robert Wright concludes in his study on *The Evolution of God* that "history seems to be guided ... in a moral direction ... toward the good."[14]

> The Global Crisis of Maturity requires us to bring our spiritual lives under control, much as we tamed nature with farming, created material abundance, organized global institutions and harnessed the power of information and knowledge.

---

14    Wright, *The Evolution of God* (New York: Little Brown, 2009)

Still, this transition will not happen without human action, and I think it is likely to require a revolution in thought and spirit. All stages in the LCE were driven by revolutions – the Agrarian Revolution, the Industrial Revolution, the Post-Industrial Revolution, the Information Revolution. Today, the passage to an Age of Consciousness requires a Mental/Spiritual Revolution powered by our old friends, technologies of consciousness (ToCs). The power of sophisticated IT systems was almost non-existent until roughly five decades ago until it appeared almost suddenly without warning. Now, we may be surprised once again to witness the power of ToCs as they gain traction in a few years.

The logic of the LCE makes this forecast compelling. Each of the above technology revolutions produced a major shift in consciousness, so spiritual transformations have been occurring throughout civilization. For instance, the famed sociologist Max Weber found that the Industrial Revolution and the spirit that drove capitalism resulted from the Protestant Reformation. It should not be surprising that another spiritual revolution could start the Age of Consciousness.[15]

This does mean the Mental/Spiritual Revolution will be quick, shocking or destructive. A mature global order of 10 billion industrialized, educated people struggling to overcome the MegaCrisis could evolve normally out of the urgent need for mutual understanding, cooperation and the shared purpose of a global community. It could also be called a New Global Order, a Moral Awakening or many other terms, and it could evolve out of a Global Ethics.

This may seem unlikely today as the world teeters at the brink and autocrats shred the global order, but things looked a lot more dismal during WWII. Germany and Japan were intent on exploiting the newfound powers of industrialization to gain world control. Yet, they were defeated by the superior industrial power of the allied forces. Today, the battle is not one of industrial might but of changing consciousness. Autocrats are testing the new powers of mass media to control public opinion, and they too will likely be overturned as human spirit triumphs. As the eternal battle between good and evil rages, this time it will be fought using ToCs, the ultimate source of power.

---

15    Jeff Warren, "Enlightenment: Is Science Ready to take It Seriously?" (*Psychology Today*, Nov 2012).

In an analysis on the rise of autocrats, political analyst Robert Kagan noted: "What can be done through social media and AI transcends even the effective propaganda of the Nazis and Soviet communists."[16]

Even now, a higher form of consciousness is rising out of the need to withstand a more difficult world. Globalization is tearing up the environment, so people are moving toward ecologically safe practices and a sustainable global order; if we move too slowly, the occasional collapse of an ecosystem and its human population will serve to prod us along. These threats are forcing corporations to reshape themselves into democratic enterprises that better serve both economic and social interests. As health care applies a growing arsenal of high-tech medicine with limited success, practitioners may be forced to unify the treatment of body and spirit. And relentless technological advances are bringing threats from breakthroughs that must be managed wisely by more enlightened humans. AI is a powerful force, but it is hard to believe the MegaCrisis will be resolved by smart machines.

All of the nagging problems that now seem insoluble – climate change, inequality, risky finances, terrorism, poverty, war – basically flow out of today's state of consciousness, and previous chapters have shown how people are altering consciousness. It's hard to believe an Age of Consciousness is possible, but we didn't anticipate the Information Age, either. When the first PCs arrived a few decades ago, who would have imagined that average people would spend their days staring into smartphones and computer screens?

The great challenge now facing civilization is to accept this mysterious power of consciousness and use it to guide our complex lives more carefully and with greater meaning. This humble but all-important task is the sacred ground on which an Age of Consciousness is being built.

The next chapter explores this new frontier in depth, offering examples, trends, and guidelines outlining how we can cope in a high-tech world by drawing on ToCs. Without getting theological, we focus on the everyday challenge of embracing our innate human spirit in more constructive, powerful and satisfying ways. By doing so, we as individuals can contribute to the creation of a mature world.

---

16    Robert Kagan, "The Strongmen Strike Back" (*Washington Post*, Mar 17, 2019)

# CHAPTER EIGHT

# Managing Our Minds: Living and Working in Spirit

I t's one thing to understand the need for changing consciousness, but to actually live and work in an Age of Consciousness requires a change of values, beliefs and purpose. It is *beyond knowledge*. The following example illustrates the power of a fully aware leader and of extending this heightened consciousness to others:

A few years ago, the chairman of Aetna defused an audience of angry shareholders by wading into the crowd and asking forgiveness for his mistakes and shaking hands with the critics. Here's how a board director described the result: "In 15 minutes he changed the mood of that entire room. It was one of the most skillful demonstrations I have ever seen."[1]

This special ability to influence people shows that higher forms of consciousness are likely to become common because they are more effective in working relationships. As we saw in Chapter Five, leaders need to cultivate humility, have faith in themselves and foster a spirit of collaboration to guide followers successfully. Only when we have reached this heightened state of mind can we spread it to others. But the place to begin is with oneself.

The previous chapters showed how the move beyond knowledge is transforming business, politics, education and religion. Now we explore how life is likely to be experienced over the next few decades. And learn how to overcome obstacles and rise above disorder under very trying circumstances.

We first look at the stressful mode of life emerging as everything becomes digitalized – I call it TeleLiving. Then we examine the technologies of consciousness (ToC) being used to develop higher-order awareness. Finally, we will consider how our individual shifts in consciousness can help guide society through the Global Crisis of Maturity.

## The Challenge of TeleLiving

Technology gave us the telephone, television, telework, and other forms of life lived through information technology. Now we have what I call "TeleLiving" – shopping, working, education, health care, spirituality and even sexual relations are all moving online.[2] These transactions will soon take place in graphic 3-D/holographic video dialogues between people, letting robotic avatars handle the busywork.

1   Ben White, "SEC Nominee Donaldson Has History of Calming Investors Fury" (*Washington Post*, Dec 11, 2002)

2   Halal, "TeleLiving" (*Futurist*, Mar–Apr, 2003)

Over the coming years, all social functions seem likely to move into a virtual world that is ever-present and intelligent. You might buy something by talking with a virtual robot that greets you by name, knows all the merchandise and displays it on demand, answers questions, takes payment and has infinite patience – the perfect salesperson. I am eagerly awaiting the development of AI to the point where a virtual robot could take the place of physicians, teachers, lawyers and almost any other knowledge worker.

The Age of Consciousness seems destined to bloom into an ethereal existence where virtual social activity becomes richly ever-present. We will have to struggle with environmental disasters and a shifting climate, pioneer high-technology markets that are changing constantly and negotiate difficult relationships to fend off conflicts. Life is not going to be easy.

As daily life moves online, it brings new sources of stress, loss of personal contact and emotional disorders. With everyone staring into screens at all hours, including during family dinners, it is little surprise the World Health Organization warned that Internet addiction is now considered a mental disorder. The problem is most acute among teens, who are spending as much as 40 hours a week on the web (equivalent to a full-time job).

This harried lifestyle translates into chronic sleep deprivation, less contact with friends and family, and serious increases in depression and suicide.[3] One-third of employees in the US suffer from chronic stress, and suicide and drug overdoses now exceed car crashes as a major cause of death. In Europe, 40 percent of the population has some form of mental illness. Ninety-five percent of human resource leaders think burnout is sabotaging the workplace.[4]

And trends suggest it could get worse. The vaunted "gig economy" of on-demand jobs could isolate a third of the labor force into digital cells working alone. Uber, TaskRabbit, Handy, Flicker and other remote employers sell on-demand services to the majority of people today, and that is likely to become widespread. While digital workers enjoy their freedom, they also are badly paid and without benefits. One said,

3    Jean M. Twenge, "Our Kid's Lives Are No Video Game" (*Washington Post*, Jul 2, 2018)

4    David Kupelian, "Americans are 'Snapping' by the Millions" (*wnd*, Apr 22, 2013); Jenny Rough, "Burnout: A Modern Malaise" (*Washington Post*, Apr 2, 2019)

"These are jobs that don't lead to anything."[5] In extreme cases, a few brave souls shed their homes, jobs and family to roam the world as digital nomads living out of their laptops and suitcases. One said, "My cell phone is my house."

If you think fake news is a problem now, wait until fake *videos* become rampant, realistically showing people doing terrible things that never occurred. And lest we think faster travel in self-driving cars, high-speed trains and Elon Musk's hyperloop will reduce commute times and stress, the fact is that average daily travel time has remained at roughly 30 minutes since ancient Rome. We will simply travel greater distances throughout our local megapolis spreading from Boston to Washington, Los Angeles to San Francisco and London to Paris.

Obviously, this can't go on, so people are trying to limit online work in order to relieve stress. The tech industry is promoting the concept of "digital wellness" to help people use Internet services more carefully. In Silicon Valley where people understand the addictive nature of online life, parents are forbidding their children to use computerized devices.[6] All technologies can be used badly, and ways have to be found to limit their dangers.

The solution to stress relief requires a much-needed shift in consciousness. We are facing the need to do nothing less than learn how to manage our minds. Rather than trying to limit technology, these approaches help us surmount the stress of online life as technology use escalates. Andy Grove, former CEO of Intel, noted that "Technology always wins in the end."

## A Personal Tour Through the ToCs

With endless claims promoting different methods of self-development, what are the best ways to cultivate more powerful forms of consciousness? Box 8 outlines a quick survey of various methods, or ToCs, being used for this purpose.

5  Nathan Heller, "Is the Gig Economy Working?" (*New Yorker*, May 15, 2017)
6  Hallie Bowles, "The Digital Gap Between Rich and Poor Kids" (*New York Times*, Oct 26, 2018)

# Box 8: Technologies of Consciousness

**The Mind-Body Connection** The influence of mental attitudes is redefining medical care. Dr. Steven Locke at Beth Israel Hospital called it a "revolution" akin to penicillin, while Dr. Sandra Levy at the Pittsburgh Cancer Institute thinks the evidence is now "indisputable" and "could change the entire face of medicine." Medical schools now practice acupuncture, meditation, mindfulness and other alternative treatments, and half of Americans use them.[7]

**Spirituality is Productive** Spiritual practices are used in the workplace because they produce results. Lawrence Perlman, CEO of Ceridian, said, "Ultimately, the combination of head and heart is a competitive advantage." Executives at Aetna, Monsanto, McKinsey, Medtronic and Silicon Graphics meditate daily. A "spiritual audit" of 200 corporate leaders found "spirituality is one of the most important determinants of performance."[8]

**Mindfulness** This more "active" form of meditation has become roaringly popular because it helps focus on what we are experiencing and directing our behavior. The benefits have drawn millions of people to use various programs like Headspace and other methods that help people meditate. Peter Diamandis, the futurist entrepreneur, helps people craft one of several "mindsets" to activate the life they choose.[9]

**The Boom in Yoga** This ancient practice has grown into a major industry of $20 billion in annual revenue. The leading magazine *Yoga* has grown to a half-million readers and 40 million Americans have adopted the discipline.[10]

**Psychotropic Plants** The war on drugs is ending as 30 nations now accept some form of legal cannabis use. An experiment at Johns Hopkins University gave volunteers psilocybin (mushrooms), while a control group was given a placebo. Many of those getting mushrooms called it the most significant event of their lives. In a follow-up, 79 percent reported increased well-being, confirmed by family and friends.[11]

**Sex as Spirituality** The popularity of Viagra and online porn make it clear we've come a long way from the Victorian days of sexual repression. Freud would be amazed to see how celebrities boast of their sex lives. In one survey, 55 percent of Americans said sexuality is "an integral part of their spiritual life." Most called it "A gift from God."[12]

---

7 "The New Science of Mind & Body" (*Newsweek*, Nov 27, 2004)

8 "Human Potential" (*Executive Update*, May 2000)

9 Bret Stetka, "Changing Our DNA through Mind Control?" (*Scientific American*, Dec 16, 2014); Justin Talbot and Frieda Edgette, "Mindfulness Can Improve Strategy, Too" (*Harvard Business Review*, May 2, 2016); "Master of Mindfulness" (*Guardian*, Nov 12, 2017)

10 Karen Heller, "Are Gimmicks a Buzzkill for Yoga?" (*Washington Post*, Apr 1, 2017)

11 Greg Miller, "A Very Memorable Trip" (*scienceNOW*, Jul 1, 2008); A good reference is by Michael Pollan, *How to Change Your Mind* (New York: Penguin/Random House, 2018)

12 "God's Gift" (*Newsweek*, Oct 2, 2008)

The next few sections will take us through a few of these ToCs. Rather than an abstract analysis, I offer the views of a seasoned practitioner to provide a more personal learning experience. Throughout an adventurous life, I have tried almost everything to keep my demons at bay and grow in spiritual directions. From a childhood where money was short, through college at Purdue and grad school at Berkeley, a painful divorce, and other challenges, I tried sensitivity groups, yoga, tai chi, retreats, acupuncture, biofeedback, protests, pot, political marches, Zen, and other ToCs. I write about this subject from personal experience.

Now, let's see how to make the shifts in consciousness needed to navigate through the maze of a high-tech world. We will focus on the ToCs that are most common and useful – mediation and spiritual practices to find calmness and inner wisdom, healthy living in nature, and psychotropic drugs that boost performance and awareness. I will then show how cultivating compassionate attitudes can cut through the disorder to help cope with a more challenging world.

Although this type of spiritual development makes good sense, it is also a struggle to become more aware, fulfilled or whatever you choose to call it. Living in harmony with the spirit takes much more than finding faith in God and the other theological nostrums. It requires hard work, dedication, good habits and the inner wisdom that we all struggle to achieve.

It also highlights the difficulty of creating a mature civilization that is globally conscious and responsible. If we have so much trouble making this transition ourselves, how can we expect those with fewer resources and less flexible cultures to accomplish it? I bring this up occasionally among friends in my church, and the general feeling is that "It's OK because God's grace is everywhere, so what are you worrying about?"

I respectfully suggest that finding a way to live a spiritual sane life is the biggest challenge of our time. How can we possibly turn around the self-centered, ill-informed habits that block responsible behavior? I believe it will happen for all the reasons noted in the last chapter, but I also feel overwhelmed by the enormity of the task.

# Searching for That Inner Power

People have found endless ways to enter that inner world – meditation, mindfulness, prayer, dance, physical workouts, music, hypnosis, and an array of websites that calm the brain.[13] Almost 500 million people meditate around the world.[14]

The field has exploded with 1,000 certified Mindfulness Based Stress Reduction (MBSR) instructors in an industry that earns more than US$ 2 billion annually serving corporate clients like Google, Twitter, Facebook, General Mills, AT&T, PepsiCo and Aetna. Hundreds of studies have shown that meditation improves health and well-being.[15]

The basic goal is to release distractions and find that inner realm of peace, strength and guidance. Listen to your body, let intuition guide your thoughts, cultivate the will to exert self-control, while making sure to relax into the "true you." Each inner life is an endless source of wisdom, past trauma, uncertainty, joy, meaning, and will, the very essence of consciousness. One man put it this way: "If you need an answer, if you listen to yourself and just trust the process, the answer will come," and another said, "In my work, it is amazing how the inner voice speaks."[16]

> An executive pinpointed the reason she meditates: "I feel I am tapping into the power of the universe."

The same "spiritual laws" hold at work, which is why various spiritual practices are common in organizations of all types. Military units have used meditation and mindfulness to enhance well-being and performance for years. A veteran struggling with PTSD said, "It was the first time in so long that I felt hope. I got my life back." It is not well known that many business groups gather in prayer before meetings. In a review of business applications of this trend, the authors of a journal article concluded: "In some cases, the more spirited companies claim to outperform others dramatically."[17]

---

13    Ariana Eunjung Cha, "New Gadgets Claim to Zap Brain into New Attitudes" (*Washington Post*, Mar 30, 2016)

14    "How Many People Meditate?" (*Mindfulness*, Dec 15, 2018)

15    Kate Pickert, "The Mindful Revolution" (*Time*, Feb 3, 2014)

16    Daniel McGinn, *Psyched Up* (New York: Penguin, 2017)

17    Lonnae O'Neal Parker, "Prayer and Profits" (*Washington Post*, Jan 11, 2002); "Marines Expanding Use of Meditation Training" (*Washington Times*, Dec 6, 2012); Caroline Winter, "Transcendental Meditation May Help Stressed Vets" (*BusinessWeek*, Feb 6, 2013); Sukumarakurup Krishnakumar, "The 'What', 'Why', and 'How' of Spirituality in the Workplace" (*Journal of Managerial Psychology*, 2002) Vol. 17, No 3

While tuning out the world and tuning into bliss is great, dealing with these inner voices can be difficult and painful. It is disturbing to face your mistakes, limitations and sins. I know from my own experience that serious prayer requires listening carefully, asking for help, and admitting the need to change. Although inspiration and guidance can be wonderful, at times when that inner voice is too demanding I wish it would leave me alone. The lives of saints are filled with agony as well as the peace that passeth understanding.

Perhaps the toughest challenge is the realization that you are not in control. It is common to spend days, even years, in a lonely search for guidance, and suddenly find it thrust on you in unexpected ways. A good example is my flash of joy while serving the homeless, as noted in the previous chapter.

But look at what has been said about the benefits of mindfulness: "Stopping to focus on the moment – on the hidden beauty of just being – is a healthy act. A calm, grateful, embodied present would improve our lives if we lived there more often," and "A calm, settled body is the foundation of health, for healing, for helping others, and for changing the world."[18]

## The Healing Balm of Nature

Beyond meditation and prayer, the next most powerful ToC is the natural world. Humans are an intrinsic part of nature, and this has produced a hereditary trait called "biophilia." Abundant studies show that the absence of nature causes a "nature deficit disorder" leading to poor health, and, conversely, the presence of a natural environment has the healing effects of "ecotherapy" or "wilderness therapy."[19]

Natural settings reduce patients' need for pain medication, increase student learning, and improve employee performance. Simply handling dirt heightens mood and enhances immune systems. One authority called it "the best therapy in the world."[20] New office buildings are designed to include plants and natural environments, and we could easily see a "greening of the workplace." The Apple headquarters is surrounded by 175 acres of

---

18    Michael Gerson, "A Quiet Room Can Silence Our Anxieties" (*Washington Post*, Mar 24, 2020); Richard Rohr, "A Settled Body" (*Center for Action and Contemplation*, Dec 29, 2020)

19    Julie Beck, "Nature Therapy is a Privilege" (*Atlantic*, Jul 23, 2017)

20    Richard Schiffman, "A Greener, More Healthful Place to Work" (*New York Times*, Jan 11, 2018)

trees and wildlife. With such benefits, it is willfully self-destructive to remain indifferent to our squandering of the environment.

For instance, my garden never fails to soothe me when I am stressed, tired, or confused. I try to walk through it each day, checking to see how my plants are doing and to make changes for their health. I clip deadwood to clear the path for new growth, pull out weeds to let in air and light, water generously and provide anything else to give them comfort. I know each tree and shrub, and I have planted most of them over many years, so they are much like pets and children. As I watch the garden grow through the seasons, I see the intricacies of life in this microcosm of the universe. Birth, death, growth, disaster, recovery, aggression, cooperation, organization, information and intelligence are all here to teach me.

My garden taught me about love. Attraction, passion and other intoxicating emotions are wonderful, but true love is being present for your loved one. It is caring for your beloved and placing their well-being above yours. One may receive love in return, but true satisfaction lies in the act of loving itself. I am thrilled at seeing my plants thrive. Grooming my garden is one of the great joys in my life, a stroll through a private, deeply cherished paradise. It gives me spiritual nourishment and soothes me in the healing balm of Nature.

## Sometimes Chemistry Is Needed

Meditation and nature are great, but sometimes our bodies need help. That's why various forms of psychotropic drug use have been constant throughout civilization, and why they are becoming legal in most parts of the world. In one study of 3,476 volunteers who took psilocybin, over two-thirds reported increased well-being, benevolence and awareness of the sacred. One year later, most called it "one of the most meaningful experiences of their lives."[21]

After centuries of medical use, pot is becoming legal again because of its benefits, the aging of the Baby Boom generation, and a growing consensus that the "war on drugs" has been a costly failure. The *Economist* magazine claims, "A global revolution in attitudes towards cannabis is underway."[22] As of 2019, Canada, Mexico,

21 Tessa Love, "The Link Between Psychedelics and Mental Health" (*Medium*, Jun 20, 2019)

22 "Where the grass is greener" (*Economist*, Aug 29, 2019)

Argentina, Belgium, Brazil, Chile, Paraguay, Peru, Germany, Spain, Switzerland, Australia, Columbia, the Netherlands, and all but six states in the US have legalized or decriminalized possession of marijuana. The Czech Republic, Portugal, and Uruguay have extended legalization to "hard" drugs such as cocaine and heroin.[23]

Much like the ending of alcohol prohibition in the 1930s, it became evident that laws against marijuana failed to discourage consumption, and the harm resulting from criminalization was overwhelming. Making pot and other drugs illegal has cost about US$1 trillion in police work over four decades, and it supports a black market of US$300 billion per year. American prisons are home to 1.6 million people, half of whom have been convicted of either selling or using drugs. And, despite fears that legalization would cause rampant drug abuse, only 6.5 percent of 12- to 17-year-olds now use marijuana, the lowest rate since 1994.[24]

> More than 1,000 world leaders, the World Health Organization, the New York Times, countless physicians, judges, and police officials have said the global war on drugs has been a disaster and called for change.[25]

The cannabis revolution is expanding to cover a variety of other psychotropic drugs in what is being called the "psychedelic renaissance."[26] Social hostesses now plan their dinner parties to accommodate vape pens with more than fruity flavors, or they may infuse a little Pineapple Express in the hors d'oeuvres. In high-tech companies, it is common to find people microdosing on pot, LSD, ecstasy, ketamine, and amphetamines. Here's how one manager described his use: "No one can afford to lose a step anymore. You want to be super lucid now."[27]

These drugs are not for everyone, and some people dislike their effects. But for many they are a Godsend. That's why many productive and famous people are known to have used pot: Carl Sagan, Herman Kahn, Willie Nelson, Bill Maher and millions

23    Michael Pollen, *How to Change Your Mind* (New York: Penguin/Random House, May 2018)

24    Rebecca Ahrnsbrak et al., *Key Substance Use and Mental Health Indicators in the United States* (US Substance Abuse and Mental Health Services Administration, Oct 5, 2017)

25    Christopher Ingraham, "More than 1,000 World Leaders Say the Drug War Has Been a Disaster" (*Washington Post*, Apr 18, 2016)

26    Matt Lamkin, "Psychedelic Medicine Is Coming" (*Scientific American*, Jul 31, 2019)

27    Kara Swisher, "Turn On, Tune In, Start Up" (*New York Times*, Aug 23, 2018)

more. It is also important to be clear that drug usage is far more than entertainment. Moderate use can be a boon to better health, well-being, inner peace and creative inspiration. Here's a small case study that captures the story of a housewife who found her way to a more loving relationship with her family:[28]

> "I never liked getting high, but a depression crippled me with anxiety and insomnia. I was already taking an anti-anxiety med, practicing yoga and exercising, and all my psychiatrist could offer was increasing my dosage. Rather than more side effects, I went to a marijuana dispensary and got advice. Now I microdose, joining the kids on the couch for a lovefest or playing a game of cards. I experience a sense of gratitude, patience and lighthearted humor, free of mental agitation. I'm a better mother because of it."

Psychotropic drugs like marijuana do not create experiences magically out of thin air. Their effects depend on the setting and inner state of mind. They release attitudes, emotions, experiences and myriad unknown bits of consciousness that are already within our bodies and alive in our souls. The effects are an interaction between the user and the drug.

I know that my use of marijuana takes me into an altered state of consciousness where the world makes sense. Beauty is everywhere, life is filled with profound meaning, and I am open to creative inspiration. It feels like I have entered the realm of spirit. While it may take months or years of meditation to reach a similar state, the beauty of pot is that Nirvana is yours almost instantly. Some of my best work has been done while in this heightened consciousness. A few ideas can seem a bit naïve later, but I have never regretted the experience.

Like all technologies, drug use can easily evolve into drug abuse. All substances can be overused, and the challenge is to avoid sheer indulgence while gaining the unique gift each can offer. Pot and other common drugs should not be used to escape reality but to enhance reality, to gain insights, relieve pain and feel whole. Excessive use is a waste of consciousness and diminishes the plant's true function.

---

28    Diana Whitney, "How Medical Marijuana Made Me a Better Mom" (*Washington Post*, Nov 17, 2018)

As mild drug use becomes normal, we should see a significant improvement in medical treatment of drug abusers, reduced crime, fewer prisoners, saved cost of police work, more taxable income, and greater tolerance of lifestyle differences. It is reported that Portugal experienced these benefits after legalizing drug use. Who knows? Legal pot might do a lot to improve everybody's mood, and maybe even ease today's dismal world situation

## Easing Life's Journey While Changing the World

These are just three methods for altering consciousness, but I think they form the holy trinity (no offense intended to fellow Christians) of useful practices. The possibilities are almost endless because everything influences consciousness – public media, culture, leadership styles, ideology and so forth. Professor Amy Cuddy at Harvard University showed that "power poses" (for instance, standing firmly as Superman or Wonder Woman) raise testosterone levels and boost confidence.

The gift of sex is among the most powerful ToCs, as evidenced by the way it leads Internet traffic to serve a massive audience around the globe. The intense power of sexual attraction continues to destroy politicians and prominent figures, and I suspect it always will. Studies show that male semen contains roughly 50 different hormones, endorphins and other mood-enhancing compounds that increase affection and mood elevation in females. These "mind–altering drugs" in semen have evolved to serve the purpose of bonding the male-female relationship,[29] once more illustrating that sex is a powerful technology of consciousness.

What stands out in all this is that there is no one best way to salvation. These are all viable paths to greater enlightenment, and we face the constant uncertainty of finding our own passage through life's journey. Mistakes and dead ends are inevitable, but we can always muddle through with perseverance and by guidance of the soul.

This may seem idealistic, but the fact is that those who cultivate attitudes of gratitude, altruism, empathy, compassion, forgiveness and love are rewarded in turn with greater happiness, health, friends and money. A study of 3,000 married couples

---

29    Jesse Bering, "An Ode to the Many Evolved Virtues of Human Semen" (*Scientific American*, Sep 22, 2010)

showed that those who take good care of their spouses lived longer themselves. People who forgave others were found to have better mental and physical health. Physicians who have "therapeutic intent" and show concern for their patients find better health outcomes.[30] Offering kindness has been shown to improve the health of your heart. Loneliness has the same effect on health as smoking cigarettes, heavy alcohol use, high blood pressure and obesity. Even fairness is a major predictor of health.[31] An important attitude is conscientiousness. Studies show that people live longer if they are responsible, organized, prudent, tenacious and otherwise able to tackle life's problems.[32]

Having *faith* in all the "goodness" values noted above is even more essential. Studies show that the benefits of any action hinge on belief and faith, whether it is the belief in a placebo that eases pain or belief in a religion. The very act of choosing some course to pursue is an act of faith. Consciousness itself flows from the realm of myth and faith. Novelist Anatole France captured this central importance of faith: "To accomplish great things, we must not only act, but also to dream; not only to dream, but also to believe."

The bottom line is to translate consciousness into action and change the world. Think of the amazing things people accomplish when they take control over their lives. The late Nelson Mandela emerged from decades of prison to lead South Africa into a multi-racial future by forgiving his captors. New Zealand's Prime Minister Jacinda Ardern had guns banned after the massacre of 41 people at a mosque, and later she smothered the 2020 pandemic to save the nation.[33] Elon Musk came from nowhere to transform online banking (PayPal), auto making (Tesla) and space travel (SpaceX). Steve Jobs, the son of an immigrant, created the smartphone and changed the world. Oprah Winfrey broke the color barrier to dominate media.

30  Frank Martela, "Exercise, Eat Well, Help Others: Altruism's Surprisingly Strong Health Impact" (*Scientific American*, Sep 7, 2018); Tom Jabobs, "Altruists Make More Money and Have More Kids" (*Pacific Standard*, Oct 18, 2018); John Tierney, "A Serving of Gratitude May Save the Day" (*New York Times*, Nov 21, 2011); Diane Ackerman, "The Brain on Love" (*Opinionator*, Mar 24, 2012); "Physician Empathy: A Cure With No Side Effects" (*Harvard Business Review*, May 12, 2010)

31  "Why Kindness Is the Key to Improved Well-Being" (*Wharton*, Sep 26, 2019); "Why Being Kind Helps You Too" (*Wall Street Journal*, Aug 11, 2020)

32  Markam Heid, "What People Who Live Long Have in Common" (*Medium*, May 17, 2020)

33  "Jacinda Ardern Consoles Families After New Zealand Shooting" (*New York Times*, Mar 15, 2019)

Steve Jobs may have been a tough leader but here's how he described his motivation in creating the smartphone: "We don't get a chance to do that many things, and everyone should be excellent. Life is brief and then you die. So, it'd better be damn good."[34]

To some, it may seem hopelessly naïve and optimistic to think of cultivating "human spirit" to foster a "mental and spiritual revolution" using "technologies of consciousness." At the time of this writing in early 2021, many nations seem lost in isolation, autocratic rule, false information and social division, and the malaise is spreading to who knows where. It's also obvious that major disasters like climate shift or deep global recession could set progress back for decades. There is plenty of reason for doubt and fear.

The main point of my argument, however, is that higher-order consciousness is likely to become more common because it is ***more effective.*** Apart from following our moral obligation to save the planet, I hope this book makes it clear that cultivating cooperation, gratitude, truth, compassion, freedom and the ideals of democracy and free enterprise are likely to prevail because these values are essential to resolve the MegaCrisis. There are certain to be fallbacks, but it seems fairly obvious that some form of higher consciousness is likely to emerge as the next phase in the Life Cycle of Evolution.

The following chapter explores the movement toward five principles of global consciousness.

# CHAPTER NINE

# Toward Global Consciousness: Start by Being Responsible

We have covered some difficult concepts in these eight chapters, and I suspect you may be feeling a bit overwhelmed and wondering what it all means. These idea have helped us understand that we are faced with a Crisis of Global Maturity, and that a global consciousness is needed make an historic passage to a world that works. This line of thought leads to the remaining question – How can we move toward global consciousness?

As I explained in the Preface, "… my work is devoted to helping all of us – especially leaders in business and government – figure out where this profound transition is heading, what it all means, and how we can get there."

This chapter amplifies the principles of global consciousness from Chapter Seven to suggest how the world can act decisively in the next few decades. Ambitious as it seems, this is a realistic vision of what's needed to survive the years ahead. It is not utopian or wishful thinking, but a definition of the basic needs for a sustainable world.

TechCast has conducted workshops with a variety of groups, explaining the problem of the Global MegaCrisis and asking for suggested solutions. After a few rounds of integrating proposed ideas into sharper focus, the following five principles emerged. We have used this framework with other groups, and it holds up well under scrutiny. Other principles are commonly suggested, but these five offer what seem to be the most useful. They are a few simple but all-encompassing statements that seem intuitively compelling. A critical mass of people acting with this type of global consciousness would create a mature civilization.

## 1. Treat the Earth and All Life Forms as Sacred

The crucial thing about the environment, contrary to all the wailing and gnashing of teeth, is that caring for the environment is a good deal. Economists expect the benefits we receive from the natural world to reach trillions of dollars annually.[1] Growth of the environmental industry is so robust that it should rank soon among the largest economic sectors, comparable to health care and transportation, which now reach US$10 trillion and US$8 trillion per year, respectively.

---

1   Paul Hawken et al., *Natural Capitalism: The Next Industrial Revolution* (Milton Park, UK: Taylor & Francis, 2010)

If we could get past the complaints about the difficulties involved, we could find that environmental management is a great opportunity in disguise. The millions of challenging green jobs alone are worth the effort, to say nothing of the benefits of a healthy environment on our entire way of life. The green bottom line is so rewarding that we should stop all the arguing and fear-mongering to simply make everything green. Ideally, every home, building, factory, product and auto could soon be designed to enhance the environment. Governments, corporations and other institutions should be held accountable for all aspects of their environmental impact.

In time, we may see a global carbon tax. The collected funds would be returned to the economy through "carbon dividends" paid to taxpayers and invested in green industries, spurring healthy economic growth. To manage this program, boards of advisors would monitor environmental conditions and set an optimal rate per ton of carbon, much as central banks adjust interest rates. In time, the entire global ecosystem will be digitized, with sensors measuring the load that individuals and corporations place on the environment and automatically sending out invoices.

---

There are some 10,000 natural halophytes, "salt plants" that grow well using seawater. These plants could produce nearly all the food, raw materials and energy that freshwater plants now produce using only wastelands and deserts. They could "green the planet" and sequester massive amounts of $CO_2$.[2]

---

We are also witnessing the strong possibility of changing the prevailing diet based on meat, which could reduce the raising of cattle that contribute seriously to climate change, while also improving health. Burger King now offers a plant-based burger that is said to be equally satisfying in "beefiness." In a blind test between a beef and a vegetable burger, one patron said of the veggie alternative: "I had no idea it was not beef." Vegetable-based foods have jumped more than 45 percent in the past few years. Just as we heard of peak oil and peak cars, now the watchword is "peak meat."[3]

---

2    Personal note from Dennis Bushnell, Chief Scientist, NASA Langley

3    David Von Drehle, "The Meat Industry Is at a Tipping Point" (*Washington Post*, Apr 7, 2019)

> The Israeli company, Hinoman, uses duckweed to create foods that are rich in protein, tasteful, nutritious and cheap. This plant can be grown year-round using very little land, water and energy. The CEO thinks "As soon as 2030, eating meat will become immoral; people will feel rather uncomfortable eating meat."[4]

Apart from the direct rewards, caring for the environment is inherently satisfying to the soul. For a simple example, composting is one of the most treasured tasks in caring for my garden. There is something natural in the ease of throwing all manner of biowaste into a compost bin and retrieving rich black soil to nourish plants in return. Closing the cycle of nature is so elementary to life that it creates a form of healing. I even recycle broken dishes, vases and ceramics by returning the pieces to stone paths running through the garden.

Sound environmental management will require a disciplined sense of responsibility for the Earth. Responsible behavior is central to any functioning society, especially in a world of raging complexity and 10 billion people who will soon inhabit our world. It is hard to see how the self-interest so rampant can survive the wrenching changes ahead; they will test everything we know.

The problem is most acute in the US, where Americans are quick to claim the rights of freedom but show little concern for their corresponding responsibilities. A TV ad for the Grub Hub food delivery system screams: "I want it all! I want it now!" With major disasters looming, we badly needed to honor both rights *and* responsibilities.

Like it or not, the MegaCrisis demands a sweeping cultural transformation that asks individuals to accept responsibility for a sustainable social order as well as for their own well-being. It will also require servant leaders who are motivated by helping others and servant followers as well. The place to begin is by becoming responsible oneself. Listen carefully to your inner wisdom and respect the sacred qualities of Nature and Mother Earth. This is your first and greatest step in helping to guide the world through the massive challenges ahead.

---

4   "Small Plant, Big Protein" (*McKinsey*, Oct 28, 2019)

## 2. Govern the World as a Unified Whole

The world is even now a *de facto* single system knit together by the billions of electronic devices forming the noosphere noted in Chapter One. But the reality of a unified globe is ignored by nations opposed to one another and unwilling to give up a bit of their sovereignty, corporations bent on profit, and individuals intent on narrow self-interest. The result is the familiar mess of global disorganization, wasteful duplication and endless conflict.

Conflict is probably the most destructive of human acts, and it benefits no one. Terrorism, violence and conflict spread like a social disease. Global consciousness accepts the need to protect oneself with defensive measures, of course, but disagreement is often a result of misunderstandings that can be resolved peacefully. Even when a result of conflicting interests, broader visions and competent leaders can often find solutions that serve both needs. Trillions of dollars are devoted to weapons and war, and a small fraction of this sum is spent on arbitration, diplomacy and peacekeeping interventions that could help curb this devastation.

The enduring conflict between Islamic radicals and white supremacists, for instance, is startling in the way each side justifies its attacks by the same attacks of the other side, often using the same language. After the New Zealand massacre of 51 Moslems by a white supremacist, the local Islamic leader said, "The Faithful cannot stand by while Muslims are burned to death." Likewise, the Christian man who murdered 11 people in a Pittsburgh synagogue in 2018 claimed, "I can't sit by and watch my people be slaughtered." As with most conflicts, both sides are locked in escalating grievances that they create out of mutual hatred, Moslem extremists condemning "white crusaders" while white supremacists blame "foreign invaders."[5]

Self-defeating hatred is not necessary nor inevitable. Charles Darwin and Adam Smith stressed the struggle to survive the battle among the most fit in nature and economics, but it is less well known that they also found a corresponding need for cooperation.[6]

---

5    For example, see an analysis of the conflict between the Islamic radicals and white extremists in "The Twin Hatreds: White Supremacy and Islamic Terrorism Are Strengthening Each Other" (*Washington Post*, Apr 7, 2019)

6    Robert Axelrod, *The Evolution of Cooperation* (New York: Basic Books, 1981)

Even Palestinians and Jews can get along well. The Palestinian Red Crescent Society and the Israeli Magen David Adom organization worked together to evacuate thousands of people from the wars in Gaza.[7]

Rather than being only a huge problem, the tendency toward conflict offers an opportunity to create millions of creative and challenging jobs to help resolve difficult situations. China, for example, has established 3,000 judges to resolve cases over environmental issues as part of the nation's strategy to build an ecologically sound civilization.[8]

A unified world does not require the "global government" that few really want and many dread. It simply requires that major actors – nations, corporations, etc. – join together in finding solutions to common problems in their enlightened self-interest.

Yet, at a time of unprecedented change, the world is adrift and lacking a vision of how to resolve these massive threats. What is needed to curtail climate change before coastal regions flood and tropical zones become uninhabitable? Can the world's collective technologies be shared for the greater good? Where can jobs be created to offset the loss of routine work that now employs half of the labor force? How can the Islamic nations find their place in a high-tech world rather than wage endless jihad? The issues needing attention are endless.

In my work as a forecaster and strategist, I see little sound strategic foresight being practiced. Apart from a general interest in talking about hot issues, the time and careful thought required often discourage serious strategic planning. Producing good strategy is hard work. It requires abstract thinking and time to cycle through problems until they can be resolved.

There is a growing industry devoted to providing strategic help, so there's a good chance we could witness a wave of sound planning to resolve the MegaCrisis. We could possibly even hope for a global dialogue that would lead us to consensus on the path ahead. That might be a useful application of our vaunted new social media.

---

7   Caroline Jaine, "Dramatic Examples of Cooperation" (*World Bank*, Apr 13, 2009)

8   James Thornton, Speech at Phillips Collection (Washington, DC: Nov 14, 2018)

The Paris Accord on climate change has the support of almost all nations – a beginning that would have been considered impossible a few years ago. Add the strategic changes noted in previous chapters – carbon taxes, collaborative politics, democratic business, student-centered education and global ethics – and we have a rough glimpse of how to govern a unified world.

## 3. Instill Democracy and Free Enterprise Throughout Institutions

Entire libraries are published, and hundreds of conferences organized each year, trying to understand the changes needed in business, government, and other institutions. The proposals are so numerous that confusion is rampant, and little progress is made to stem the loss of confidence, from the failures of democracy, to the moral crisis of capitalism, to scandals in the Catholic Church.

If we could look at the problem in light of our best traditions, we would find the solutions in our common heritage of democracy and free enterprise. As we have shown in earlier chapters, various combinations of these two fundamental principles hold the key to institutional transformation. The crisis of democracy requires encouraging centrist governments that use managed markets for public services. Corporations need to invent a democratic form of enterprise to harness the support of their stakeholders.

The main problem is that these two principles are so seldom practiced. Bureaucracy and a loss of faith in government are the primary cause of today's crisis in democracy, while the typical corporation can be accurately described as an autocratic hierarchy. The very nature of hierarchy promotes central planning, somewhat like the old Soviet Union.[9] And the ideal of competition is absent as network effects, winner-take-all economics, industry lock-in and other market flaws create *de facto* monopolies like Microsoft, Apple, Facebook, Amazon and Google.

Driven by the power of competition, corporate structures are morphing into networks characterized by agility and resilience.[10] Companies like Google are building "internal enterprises" or "self-managed teams" rewarded with incentives and free to

9    "Revealed – the Capitalist Network that Runs the World" (New Scientist, Oct 19, 2011)

10   *The Five Trademarks of Agile Organizations* (McKinsey, Jan 26, 2018)

operate outside of the normal bureaucracy. A few like eBay and Amazon have created complete internal market systems that invite entrepreneurs to compete. And with workers increasingly operating as free agents, it is easy to envision a time when self-organizing networks interact at the grassroots, while managers adjust the parameters of these systems (pay, goals, etc.) and work closely to coach business units along.[11]

We saw in Chapter Five how corporations are starting to collaborate with stakeholders instead of focusing primarily on profits for investors. The concept of "stakeholder capitalism" seems to be everywhere now, which is a great start. But the term "capitalism" remains loaded with the baggage of exploitation, self-interest and money, and this unfortunate heritage perpetuates the present system. It would help greatly to shed the name "capitalism" if we hope to realize the benefits of what should be seen as a more powerful concept of "democratic enterprise."

> Apple awards ten percent of its annual bonuses for executives based on their performance against social and environmental standards starting in 2021. Coca-Cola works with its stakeholders when launching a new product or the promotion of a new community initiative.[12]

Democracy and enterprise are likely to triumph over the long term simply because they are the most functional systems of government and economic markets. The main questions are, how, when and by whom? Americans are ideally suited for this challenge as it flows out of our heritage. We could be surprised to find today's apathy transformed into a Second American Revolution. But we could also be disappointed to see the US sink further into decline, while China, Asia, the EU and other nations take the lead. We shall see soon.

## 4. Embrace Diversity as an Asset

All the antagonisms between races, politics, religions and the many other divisions we struggle against are really, once again, opportunities in disguise. Differences are like the poles in a battery – a source of energy and power. Diversity is not a problem but an asset. By moving past our fear of those who are different, we could find new

11   William Halal et al, *Internal Markets: Bringing the Power of Free Enterprise Inside Your Organization* (New York: Wiley, 1993)

12   "Coca-Cola Team Executes Stakeholder Strategy" (*Quorum*, Dec 15, 2020)

sources of knowledge, cultural insights and solutions to intractable problems.

Good examples can be seen in nations that have embraced a wide diversity of people – the US, UK and the EU. England, for instance, has become a vibrant cultural meeting place offering the richness of India, Asia, Europe, Africa and almost all nations around the globe. Some of the best Indian cuisine is available – not in Mumbai, New Delhi or Bangalore – but in London. One of the things I treasure most about my country, the US, is that people from all over the world can become Americans. It is a joy to witness a native of China, Africa or Mexico proudly claim the rights and responsibilities of being a naturalized American.

The future can be seen vividly in university classrooms where students of all races, nations and genders share their common love of learning, hip-hop, iPhones and their very diversity. Young people today seem unaware of race or sexual identity as causes for division. Rather than being considered troublesome, their differences are celebrated. The greater the difference, the more it is intriguing. We should praise the young as they embody the multiracial societies the world is moving toward. Today's generation of youngsters are the world's first global citizens.

Multiracial marriages are becoming increasingly acceptable, even in parts of America where racism has been endemic, and they produce lovely children. When in Hawaii, I marvel at the handsome, healthy youngsters that are a blend of genes from original Hawaiians, Chinese, Japanese and Caucasians. They seem living proof that diversity is a force for good.

To realize the benefits of diversity, however, we must learn how to stop arguing and to start listening. The polarization of humanity into warring camps is a blight on society, with opposing groups stoking their opposition by accepting only information sources that reinforce their limited beliefs. The best hope for peace lies in cultivating the difficult practice of listening deeply to opponents. Most people only wait out their opponent while planning a counterattack. Really listening requires using empathy to truly understand the other's views and to alter your position by internalizing the valid points into your own thinking. Done by both sides, it can resolve differences and promote mutual understanding.

Psychiatrist and philosopher Victor Frankl, a survivor of the Nazi death camps, captured the essence of free will: "Between stimulus and response, there is a space. In that space is our power to choose a response. In our response lies our growth and our freedom."

Presently, the great challenge for many Americans is opening themselves to the views of the 74 million people who voted for Donald Trump in the 2020 elections. Those voters consider Biden anathema, but they are also a dominant force in American society. They are the source of conservative political power for the foreseeable future. If we could really listen to them, without judgment, perhaps we could come to appreciate why they distrust the "deep state," their resentment that "foreigners are taking over their country," and the other ills they see in such stark exaggeration. By truly entering their world, it becomes possible to consider policies to alleviate their valid concerns, calm legitimate fears and become friendly opponents.

As the quote above by Victor Frankl notes, we can avoid tit-for-tat battles by using our powers of free will. Instead, distance emotionally from the fray and listen carefully to understand. The admonition to "love your enemy" may sound like a hollow platitude. It does not mean that differences vanish, but that shedding hostility allows us to speak freely among adversaries with whom we disagree. Free of rancor, it is then possible to see differences objectively.

One of my best colleagues is a lovely woman and an accomplished professor, but she is also a loyal supporter of President Trump. Still, we enjoy a hearty friendship, even joking about politics. Considering the conflicts that are rampant, we certainly need common ground.

With leadership and examples of collaboration among those we disagree with, then we may see that diversity of races, religions, gender and other differences become merely superficial. That would be a far richer world for all.

## 5. Celebrate Community

The principles above are rational solutions to difficult problems, but human behavior is guided by interests that transcend logic. The World Olympics Games, for instance, are special because they provide a rare feeling of global community. Any society needs frequent opportunities to gather together in good spirit, enjoy differences and commonalities, and simply to celebrate the glory of life.

> The Rio Carnival – or Carnaval – is perhaps the biggest party on Earth. Carnaval takes place from Friday to Tuesday over the weekend before Lent. Variations are celebrated around the globe, such as Mardi Gras in New Orleans, Louisiana, USA.

As the planet is increasingly wired together, we can expect to see more global events. A rudimentary global consciousness is here now as we all share the same news events and the same struggles, although in separate niches. Automatic language translation is becoming common, and it is easy to envision global platforms like TV, Facebook and YouTube forming a wealth of connections. The formation of a global community seems inevitable, as well as celebratory events on big media platforms over the coming years. We need to nourish the global soul.

## A Case Study in Global Consciousness

To illustrate a practical application of global consciousness, I offer this little case study provided by my neighbor and good friend, Frank Staroba.

## Box 10: Case Study - Five Principles for a Dog Park

### By Frank Staroba, DFA

While reviewing draft chapters of Prof. Halal's new book, I was struck by how precisely his principles resonate with a major experience I went through in my community. Hardy Park is a beautiful green plateau in Washington, DC, that adjoins my property. After years of use, it needs renovation and does not meet the needs of all its stakeholders. The park had a serious problem with pet dogs taking over the grounds and preventing people from entering.

My neighbors and I decided to address this issue, and our first step was to accept the fact that we would have to do this ourselves. We now feel responsible for seeing it through. (Principle 1)

I am a member of the Steering Committee of Friends of Hardy, a volunteer group that cherishes and looks after the park. The committee succeeded in getting $5.2 million in the city budget for planning and construction, altering how the DC Government works. (Principle 2) This pushed the city to respond to our priorities, and they have been very cooperative.

Getting the funds has forced us to reconcile the conflicting preferences of all parties. (Principle 3) Our committee feels like a caterpillar preparing to become a butterfly. By 2022, we expect to become truly gorgeous, but first there's a lot of crawling to do. We developed a plan based on our vision for the park and on priorities from a survey we did three years ago.

Two large public meetings were held, each dominated by the dog park issue. They showed how hard it is to cooperate and arrive at consensus in a large group. However, in our small steering committee we can work by discussing and letting the leadership float, so we can reach a consensus. The process requires listening, respect, and a willingness to find common ground. Somehow, we'll arrive at a compromise because we trust the process even though it's long and frustrating. (Principle 4)

We know our efforts will green the future park and once it's finished, we will celebrate with a grand reopening. (Principle 5) Then, we'll all be butterflies.

Dr. Staroba served as Associate Dean of the College of Liberal and Fine Arts, University of the District of Columbia. He has directed or acted in more than fifty university and professional productions, and is a senior consultant for Staroba & Company

## We Are Going to Need All the Help We Can Muster.

The five principles of global consciousness presented in this chapter are proposed as a realistic approach for getting through the Global Crisis of Maturity. I am sure others can offer more good ideas. Or just use your own good judgment, and heed your inner voice. And be sure to listen carefully to your friends, loved ones and anybody who has their own worthy opinions. Given the enormity of the challenge ahead, it's important to remember that we are all in this together, and we are going to need all the help we can muster.

# CHAPTER TEN

# Evolution's Climax: The Flowering of Human Spirit

I hope this book has shown that the great issues of our time mark the next phase in the Life Cycle of Evolution.

From this perspective, existential threats like climate change are not simply great problems – they begin our passage to a sustainable civilization. AI, robotics and other intelligent products of the technology revolution are more than dangerous new powers – they promise to eliminate routine mental work and open a creative frontier of more fulfilling lives. The current plague of autocrats, isolationism and fake news is discouraging – but it warns us that we must shape our collective consciousness. All these Herculean challenges are more than a great mess – they are integral parts of the passage to a mature global order.

With this global shift in outlook, the impossible problems blocking our path become solvable: centrist politics and government markets could rejuvenate nations; corporate communities that engage stakeholders can create social and financial value; student-centered education helps to learn higher-order skills; and global ethics could form a global consciousness to unify diverse cultures into a world that works.

The following scenario sums up the key points of how the Age of Consciousness is likely to unfold in the years ahead. It is designed to help us grasp the details and feel the texture of the emerging world of consciousness. Other outcomes are possible, of course, but based on the evidence presented in this book, I think this is most likely. It is the natural climax in the Life Cycle of Evolution.

## Box 11: Most Likely Scenario - 2030

### The Flowering of Human Spirit

The decade of the 2020s proved critical as scorching heat, drought, wildfires, floods and violent storms devastated the Earth, leaving parts of the southern US, Middle East, Africa and Asia uninhabitable. More pandemics flared up occasionally, and the resulting economic disruption caused the global depression that had long been feared as national debt reached stratospheric levels.

Climate-change refugees from Arabic nations, and some Europeans, stormed the Nordic nations and Russia looking for relief from the heat, while Mexicans and people from the southern US states fled to Canada. With warming temperatures, even Siberia became a much sought-after place to live. At the Eastern seaboard of the US, the costs for building sea walls reached trillions of dollars. Still, New York City struggled to subdue chronic flooding in the subways and at street levels, much like Venice. Public riots soon forced politicians to take serious steps to curtail $CO_2$ emissions. Forecasts for the coming years were even more severe, creating a global shift of opinion to resolve the climate crisis, finally.

With the Trump era over, the political pendulum made its normal corrective turn to the left, supported by women rising to power, growing ethnic populations, low-paid workers and youngsters who demanded change. But in time there was an appreciation of the need for collaboration as the only way to reconcile differences with Trump's supporters. Biden and his successor, Kamala Harris, moved to the center and found ways to integrate the interests of conservatives with those of liberals, producing historic breakthroughs.

Corporations began adopting the broader social role advocated by the Business Roundtable, the World Economic Forum and other influential institutions. Corporate CEOs began working with environmentalists, communities, their employees and customers to address major social problems. Wall Street opposed these changes, but progressive firms demonstrated that stakeholder collaboration was actually good for the bottom line, and the threats were so severe there was little choice. Bill Gates, Warren Buffett and Mitt Romney met with President Biden at the height of the crisis. The result was a "New American Deal," a modern version of FDR's New Deal that helped alleviate the Great Depression.

By 2025, a majority of corporations, with the well-publicized support of many billionaires, adopted a "democratic" form of free enterprise, and positive results set off a swell of interest in the powers of collaboration. Artists portrayed the major stakeholder groups as a five-pointed star uniting all interests - like the stars on the American flag. The five-pointed star became an iconic symbol, much like Apple Company's logo of an "apple with a missing bite" and Facebook's "thumbs up for a like." After decades of being viewed as social pariahs by many on the left, business leaders became accepted as heroes leading the way to a more humane form of economics.

The right accepted the new democratic form of enterprise, while the left yielded its demands for increased regulation in favor of a more self-governing private sector. The next few years saw a new social contract in which business began solving massive problems while also making good profits at less risk, and government was relieved of its burden for managing what seemed like everything. Many Republicans got on board also. It seems a watershed has been crossed from conflict and hostility to cooperation and amity. Hard to believe, but we seem to be living in a new "collective consciousness."

The power of this mental shift became fairly obvious, and the US found itself providing world leadership once again. A global plan soon brought the US, China, the EU and other major nations together to help developing regions create sustainable industries. These transformative changes were supported by the new breed of "creative workers" who emerged as most jobs now required leadership, social problem-solving and coordination. Process facilitators and mediators were appointed to resolve differences and forge creative solutions.

Various proposals were considered for adopting a standard of global ethics to govern the planet as a coherent community. Prospects look good for creating what is being called "a unified world that works." The result has been a palpable shift to a global consciousness that made impossible obstacles melt away as people embraced common values, forming the global web of spirit envisioned long ago. Teilhard de Chardin became a popular media star.

Green technologies, environmental research and knowledge were shared. A global green tax was adopted, with revenues to be returned to taxpayers. And with millions of high-tech jobs opening up in environmental work to replace positions lost to automation, the global economy entered a period of clean growth, including developing nations. It was estimated that "peak $CO_2$," or "peak warming" was likely to be reached about 2034, starting the long process of cooling the Earth. People began to believe they could cooperate around the world, and it became possible to see the prospect for a unified global order. It can't happen soon enough.

This scenario may seem optimistic, and many of the details will inevitably be proven wrong. There are many possible paths through this crisis. Even the collapse of civilization is possible, or its degradation into a high-tech Dark Age. Some scientists interpret the striking lack of evidence for alien life after 50 years of searching to mean that most societies fail to surmount environmental disaster and other aspects of the Global MegaCrisis. So, this is a test of survival for civilization on planet Earth.

Still, I hope this scenario shows that a global transformation is not only possible but even reasonable. The direction of the Life Cycle of Evolution points logically to an Age of Consciousness as the culminating phase of civilization. It is rather obvious now that the world cannot continue its current path, and we should see a Mental/Spiritual Revolution or some similar breakthrough at about 2025 or so.

The next several years seem destined to be critical. Life may go through the normal rhythms of work, family, entertainment, but it will become far more intense as humanity faces life-or-death struggles to resolve the MegaCrisis. Yet, one way or another, this decade will be a moment of truth for civilization, much like that crucial point when a teenager becomes an adult, or a child is born. The pressures now forcing the global transition will become too urgent to allow delay. Teilhard de Chardin noted that the rise of consciousness is "all creation groaning in this one great act of giving birth." That act is beginning today. By 2030, it will be obvious to all.

A functioning Global Order along these lines is likely to appear at about 2050 +/- 10 years. In fact, I am as confident in this forecast as I was in the 1970s that the Knowledge Age would arrive about 2000. And it showed up right on time! Physicist Michio Kaku thinks we are on the verge of reaching a Type I planetary civilization.[1]

---

1   "When Will We Advance to a Type I Civilization on the Kardashev Scale?" (gaia.com, Jun 27, 2017)

Although the historic evidence leads to the flowering of human spirit, there are good reasons for doubt and to face other possibilities. Ultimately, we each have to make an existential choice: Which side of history do you want to be on? To frame this question in more active terms, What type of future do you want to create?

Made in the USA
Middletown, DE
28 February 2022